THE
SURVIVAL
HANDBOOK

The Survival Handbook

How to save
your skin when
disaster strikes
without warning

By
Anthony
Greenbank

Bell & Hyman

First published by Wolfe Publishing Limited 1967
This revised edition published 1985 by
Bell & Hyman Limited
37–39 Queen Elizabeth Street
London SE1 2QB

British Library Cataloguing in Publication Data

Greenbant, Anthony
 The Survival handbook.
 1. Wilderness survival   2. Outdoor life—
 Safety measures
 I. Title
 613.6[9   GC200.5

 ISBN 0–7135–2514–2

Illustrations by Christopher Evans
Cover design by Colin Lewis
Designed by Neil Sayer

ISBN 0 7135 2514 2

Typeset by Inforum Ltd, Portsmouth
Printed in Great Britain by
Cox & Wyman Limited, Reading

ALL THE FOLLOWING ADVICE
PRESUPPOSES THAT
WHOEVER FACES CATASTROPHE
TAKES A DEEP BREATH
AND MAKES UP THEIR MIND
TO HAVE A REALLY DETERMINED GO
TO BEAT THE ODDS
AT ALL COSTS

Contents

Preface

This book is about how to survive. How to live through almost every conceivable accident or disaster that our dangerous world can produce.

Accidents and disasters, of course, *can't* happen to you. But they do. Every day. To thousands of people like you, whose only really nightmarish experience was their last.

Fires, flood, earthquakes, out-of-control cars, crashing trains, sinking ships ask no questions. Winds, rain, snow, ice, burning sun make no exemptions. Lost in a mountain mist, wandering thirst-crazed in a desert, freezing to death in a blizzard, the fact that it can't happen to you makes no difference. It *is* happening.

When it does happen, you probably won't have this book in your coat pocket. You'll be lucky if you have a coat at all. But after reading this book you will be mentally equipped. Equipped to escape the immediate danger. Equipped to stay breathing until help arrives. Equipped to survive.

To live through an impossible situation, you don't need the reflexes of a Grand Prix driver, the muscles of a Hercules, the mind of an Einstein. You simply need to know what to do.

The Survival Handbook is a textbook of what, in an increasingly complex and dangerous world, has become a new science.

The book contains nothing but information. Tight-packed, factual information. No cheap thrills. No heroes. No heroics. Just hard facts. Which, we hope, will enable many youngsters to live to be parents, many parents to live to be grandparents and many grandparents to live out, peacefully, their natural life span.

Introduction

The Survival Handbook is like no other. It gives a man, his wife and children a fighting chance in any catastrophe at a time when – as any newspaper will tell you – the chances are they will succumb and die. It is not a do-it-yourself James Bond manual, for it assumes no advance preparation except reading it.

People *are* growing softer today. Elements of modern-day living not only make us more vulnerable: they fatten for the kill. Read the headlines: 'careering car wipes out newly-weds'; 'rogue train annihilates 37 commuters'; 'crowd at spectator sport crushes 9'; 'flaming electric blanket murders family'; 'unseen knifing in dark discotheque'; 'veering plane massacres 24 holidaymakers' . . .

Existing survival books go strongly on the mountain, desert, jungle, arctic and ocean scene. They are useless to the family facing an onrushing tide and trapped by cliffs, or to the bookmaker whose car is trapped among moorland snowdrifts miles from anywhere. Not only are they unlikely to have read them; if they had, the pertinent information – wrapped among graphs, tables, case histories, maps and bibliographies – would be almost impossible to recollect.

Most of us have only the vaguest idea of survival. If thought about at all, it is by some quaint rule of thumb (does one pour petrol on frostbitten fingers – No!). We face the bitterest winters at home with equanimity – and are surprised, shocked and hurt when threats of exposure and frostbite turn into a reality.

This book deals with *crises*. Prevention is better than cure, but no one is immune from human or mechanical failure, or Act of God. Hence the stress on *when* catastrophe hits home – *when* car is submarining to bottom of lake, *when* intruders are binding you hand and foot, *when* eyes are blinded. Where possible, prevention is treated too – in note form.

People would never remember in a crisis? Not usually so! Fed with a drill to save its skin, the brain grabs that plan by the scruff of the neck. True, the girl whose arms are already pinned by an assailant cannot produce the comb which might save her, but let her hear him first, padding behind her along the pavement, and she could.

Instead of being mesmerized with fright, you are more likely to be ready and braced in a sudden crisis after reading this book than before. In a fight for life lasting weeks your subconscious would automatically reach back for help from its pages. To this end, mnemonics (memory-fixers) are incorporated in the very layout of the book by using entry headings unique in survival theses to-date.

Human feelings are the key. Pitched into catastrophe they cry for warmth or cold or water or dry land or shade or light or speed or slowness regardless of whether dazzling glare is from H-Bomb or headlights, stifling heat is in desert or burning house, choking contamination is radiation or carbon monoxide. This book is arranged to rally these feelings by grouping remedies under them: firemaking under *Too Cold*, car collision drill under *Too Fast*. And so on.

No entry here presumes that you are prepared. When crisis looms – *that's it*! There is *you* (bone/skin/hair/teeth/nails/saliva), your possessions (shoes/socks/pants/skirt/frock/watch/possibly cash, comb etc.), the surroundings (sand/rock/water/trees/concrete/guano) and quite often wrecked transport (car/plane/train/boat). Desert captives are not allowed to find a handy sheet of plastic for a water-still, though if they have one all ready its use is shown – but well down the list of water-seeking methods.

The theme of *The Survival Handbook* is not so much 'be prepared' as be *prepared to improvise with anything*. When 'everything' seems so slight as to be ridiculous, think of rescuers saying: 'If only he'd wrapped up in those newspapers . . .' This book takes it for granted you have nothing rather than something . . . but if you have something, use it.

Using this book we suggest you (i) anticipate trouble ahead in likely places (football match/plane flight/rush hour traffic) by checking in the Index under the appropriate heading, then turning to the relevant pages for advance briefing (ii) read the book more than once so that in sudden fire/flood/tempest/earthquake you increase your chances of surviving. And as an extra aid the entries are linked by cross-references – climbing from sea into boat comes in *Too Low*, but getting to that boat happens in *Too Wet*. Hence there is a cross-reference to link them.

Survivors will always live to tell of surviving by doing just the opposite of others who have also survived! Medical experts have often told survivors that by all rights they should be dead. Instead of dying they had the *will* to live. *You too must enlist this will*, that sense of self-preservation which starts with a deep breath and the determination not to give way at any cost.

People are growing softer today – yes; but it is a cheering fact that, given a plan of action, even though despairing and shocked, people can and do react well in crises. Once the initial shock has lessened you stand every chance of becoming a survivor if, as we suggest, you give yourself a regular servicing by re-reading this, a kind of maintenance handbook.

Too
Lonely

1 Too Lonely

Anyone facing extinction feels the loneliest person on earth. You are as alone in the rioting football crowd, squashing air from your lungs, as on a raft at sea.

The anatomy of loneliness is a skeleton. Jerking muscles, scrabbling fingers, shivering marrow, straining sinews – these are the bare bones of panic and initial despair.

Survival of the fittest does not mean you have to be physically perfect. Stripped to a clawing puppet by crisis, everyone is reduced to an isolation where survival is all in the mind.

Aspects of Loneliness

Mental

Taking a deep breath and making up your mind to have a really determined go at beating the odds at all costs is the vital factor in survival.

When initial shock brings utter despair it is still possible for that sense of self-preservation to pull you through, though you may be totally disorientated and terrified.

If contemplating giving in or suicide: prayer is a proven help. The Lord is my shepherd . . . though I walk through the valley of shadow of death . . . Thy rod and staff comfort me . . . the 23rd Psalm is a proven favourite (most can remember the words in some form or other).

Other pleas range from the Catholics's O my God relying on Thy infinite goodness . . . and the Jewish Hear, O Israel, the Lord our God . . . to a universal O God, get us out of this lot.

Run/drive/signal/swim/make fires/build shelter/signal again . . . all the harder. Don't lie down to die without a fantastic struggle first. Never ever give in.

Tell yourself: even this will pass.

In unknown environment improvise, improvise, improvise.

Never never never never never never never never never give up trying. Out of all the untidiness, quickness and/or dragging slowness of survival, salvage, clutch and spur your vital instinct of self-preservation.

Desperation

Alcoholics Anonymous. The Samaritans. Dial-a-Prayer. Citizens Advice Bureau . . . all are typical organizations available by telephone which have prevented suicides when contacted by someone in deep trouble.

Directory Enquiries will help in such circumstances all over the world: an operator helping you from local knowledge.

Dial 999 only for Fire/Police/Ambulance/Coastguards and Lifeboat/Mountain or Cave Rescue.

Claustrophobia

Very unpleasant feeling. The real thing grips trapped people in proper panic. Will do something rash/scream/kick/hammer place down/rave/fight. Very few suffer from real claustrophobia; very many think they do.

Restrain anyone so gripped with fear (so they don't hurt themselves or you). Comfort. Calm. Reassure. Only slap in face or render unconscious if situation out of control.

Count blessings. **One** – I'm alive. **Two** – (probably) not injured. **Three** – can last several days without food and water so long as not using energy. **Four** – only a matter of time before they find me. **Five** – keep keeping cool.

Check pockets/handbag/surrounds for food/matches/keys/nailfile/lighter – anything that may help to scratch/dig/screw/signal way out.

Improvise lavatory from stones/holes/rubbish/clothing. If nothing (say in lift) make sponge from clothing/newspaper etc.

Agoraphobia

Fear of open or public places (rarer than claustrophobia) also brings terror. Dizziness/sickness/fainting seizes victims. Can come gradually or in sudden panic.

It is no cure to be told to 'Snap out of it.'

Get *inside* (bus/shop/cinema) if attacked by agoraphobia. Buy magazine and bury head in it until you get home.

If prone to attacks always carry a 10p piece *and* a 5p piece for telephone call for help to friends or relatives.

Imagination

Terror can mount in the dark/gloom/shade (*see Too Dark page 120*).

Fight it down. Get a grip. Rationalize the things-that-go-bump/things-that-go-flash/things-that-touch-you. They usually have ordinary explanations.

As with, for example, a lonely house you are beginning to feel is haunted; the following are likely causes . . .

> House is built above underground watercourse
> Machinery in locality sets up vibrations
> Echoes from next door
> Roof/walls/floors expanding or contracting
> Tight-fitting doors making air traps of each room
> Reflections from passing cars/trains/planes
> Tree branches scraping on window
> Cats/mice/starlings-in-the-attic
> Green wood in house structure groans and creaks
> Slate off roof makes wind moan
> Airlock in water pipes makes thumping noise

To reassure yourself make a ghost-check when daylight comes. Inspect all house (cupboards/chimneys/attic). Seal off rooms and windows. Tie black cotton across stairs/landings/doors. Pans of water on floors show vibrations. Shake out dust/sand/powder on floors.

Final consolation: a *real* ghost . . .

(a) Will disappear if you approach it.

(b) Can do you no physical harm because it leaves nothing earthly – not even messages or footprints.

(c) Will not cast a shadow; will look quite substantial rather than misty; will not ignore you; will not carry its head tucked under an arm.

(d) Is all in *your* mind anyway.

How to get Help

How *do* you call *Help*! successfully today when the tendency is for passers-by to cross to the other side of the road in case you are (a) part of the Esther Rantzen team (b) going to make them look foolish anyway (c) going to get them killed? How *do* you say SOS successfully miles from civilization?

Use everything. Screams. Whispers. Shouts. Sign language. Red triangle. Whistles. Bonfires. Matchlight. Telephone 999. Bang central heating pipes/car horn/doors. Wave clothes. Flash mirror. Throw stones. Keep whistling kettle on boil. Toll bell. Blow bugle. Smash glass. Fly kite. Pull communication cord. Light candle. Bang head/shoes/fists on wall.

Note: don't endanger *yourself* (e.g. rush to toll church bell, unschooled in the art, and you will be rocketed up by rope to crack skull on ceiling).

Peculiar crises – unorthodox signals. Trapped on moonlit roof yank away TV aerials. Giving kiss of life in express train compartment throw note (weighted with ballpoint pen) on passing station platform begging ambulance ready at next stop (pulling communication cord would waste time). On tailboard of speeding hijacked lorry, go mad until some driver slows, winds window down and you shout *Police!*

Don't rely on one method. Yell *and* shake curtain. Whistle *and* flick cigarette lighter. Whisper to garage attendant that your passenger has gun *and* break law in front of police car. Use sign language *and* break glass. Light fire *and* wave. Erect red triangle on road *and* set fire to oily rags.

Pick best position (if possible). By window. On higher ground. On open snowfield (but never on a *steep* slope). By chink blowing draught through roof-collapse rubble. Under gap in tree top canopy. On boat's mast.

Select your signals. Save energy (shouting and waving), torch batteries, matches, bonfire fuel when far from view and earshot until help approaches. Keep them in reserve, dry and ready to use instantly. Meanwhile signal with: flags, markers, shadow writing, dust clouds, mirror.

Never give up. Keep signalling until answered, no matter how long that is.

Ways of Signalling

Flags
Rip sheets, shirts, coat linings – any material not used directly for clothing or shelter. Fly flags from sticks, poles, windows, roofs, conspicuous trees.

More chance of success when waved. Try for contrast with background: red, orange, yellow against snow, or dirt-smeared cloth if only white available. Keep it flying all the time. Fly a kite when you have line/ handkerchief/coat/wind. Practise – a distress kite can carry a fishing line too (*see Too Empty page 273*). Note: twigs/saplings/wire/framework is 'bowed' away from cloth.

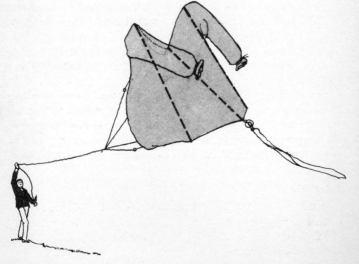

Fig 1 Kite made from a coat

Balloons
A protective sheath inflates to knee height and floats, or can be hung from tree branches/chimney pots/rock face as good distress signal. Reflects radar.

Markers
Use anything that is static to draw attention. Crashed plane, beached boat, stranded car. They are better seen from the air if the top surfaces are clean and – where applicable – polished. Clear away snow, sand, foliage. Trample, ravage, spoil and burn surrounds to make conspicuous. Spread rocks into noticeable formations. Deposit rubbish to litter the scene. Lay anything that glints or is bright on top of plane or vehicle. Polish bright surfaces with sand or gravel.
  Important:
(a) *Getting out* from a crash scene far from civilization is always to be desired and preferred to digging-in/making wooden spoons/playing Boy Scouts.

  But *only* leave the marker of plane (or other transport) wreck in favour of trekking for help if you stand a good chance of reaching inhabited croft/igloos/tents/huts/hydro-electric power station/shooting lodge/settlement/town/city.

  And *only* if you are in fit enough state to travel, if no chance at all of being seen on crash site from the air, and if you make preparations first for the trek out (*see Too Slow page 228*).

  Otherwise stay until found. Very many have died after forsaking immbolized transport for a desperate cross-country trip.
(b) If living in snow holes or soundproof shelters which blanket the sound of passing aircraft always, if conditions permit, have someone 'on watch' in an open-topped shelter right among the markers to listen and possibly mirror-flash too.

Writing
With nail varnish/keys/pebble/nailfile/soot/blood/charcoal/cinders/soap/grease . . . on slate/stone/dirty car/inner birch bark/walls/cloth/plastic/tin . . . in dust/snow/sand/mud.
  Write SOS on glass (if not in position to smash it)

with finger/fingernail/lipstick if glass is clear/misted/ frosted. To make it readable from other side write ZOZ (and round off Zs to make about-turn Ss). Also write ꟼ⅃ƎH And add anything to qualify: ƎᴚƎH NI ƎVI⅃A MA.

Write SOS message on paper and fold it into a dart (as shown). Flight it for busiest street, say, when trapped high in a building.

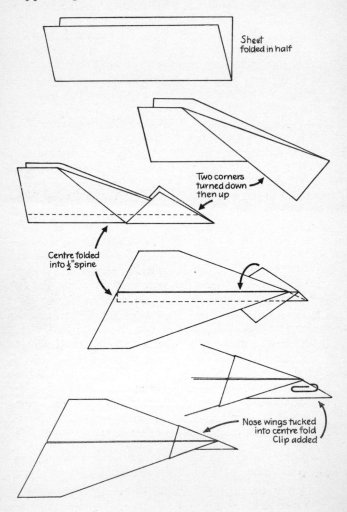

Fig 2   SOS dart

On a bigger scale, and miles from anywhere . . .

Shuffle out letters SOS (shadow writing) in snow 6m–9m (20 ft – 30 ft) tall. Deepen tracks into broad channels, and pile the snow from these where they will cast the sun into long shadows along the letters. Increase size of these drifts with underlayer of rocks. Stress shadows with soil, leaves, branches, stones. A good shadow sign can be seen from aeroplane on moonlit night. (*See also Potassium Permangante page 154.*)

Fig 3   Shadow writing

Shadow writing can be used in sand.

Where neither snow nor sand, use rocks, tree branches and sods to build low walls to shadow letters SOS. Again sculpt for shadows with leaves, debris, soil in the shadow areas. Shovel any patches of snow (in timber country) into letters to stress shadows.

Noise

When making a noise remember . . .

(a) Shout only when likely to be heard (say when stuck in old-fashioned lift with collapsible gates). It takes up energy/makes thirsty/roughens throat.

(b) Keep quiet at intervals to hear any sound of others.

(c) Whistles really carry. Practise shepherd's technique of putting two fingers in mouth while imprisoned and awaiting rescue (put either first two fingers or the 1st and 3rd fingers of one hand

19

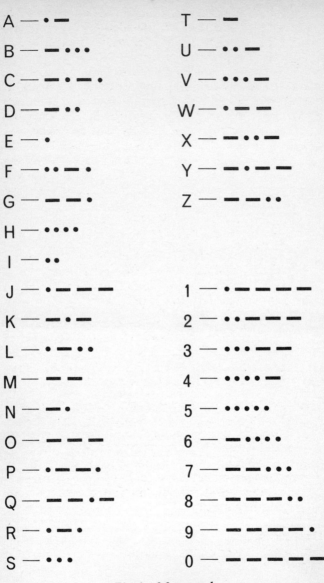

Fig 4   Morse code

against tip of tongue in mouth and try to whistle through narrow gap of these fingers. Don't press tongue too hard back. You may be successful in time.).

How do you wet your whistle when scared? (It's difficult to salivate when fear-gripped.) Licking lips/rolling tongue/sucking thumb or pebble helps. Also – picture biggest steak/salad/oyster platter – or whatever dish is your favourite.

(d) Use best conductor of sound – say, tapping metal pipes with hand-held dentures (if nothing else) when buried in building rubble. You don't *have* to know the morse code. Just keep tapping/scratching/thumping.

(e) Smash glass for sound outlet. If nothing (not even shoes) for a club use a fist thus:

1. **Wrap something round wrist.**
2. **Punch straight – knuckles uppermost.**
3. **Hold fist rock steady after impact.**
4. **Withdraw hand very gingerly.**

(f) Shout *help!* in a low, booming tone. The low help call is heard long after a whistle is inaudible (hence Big Bertha bullhorns guide lost hunters in USA forests). Jamming fingers in ears actually helps you call even louder than usually possible.

(g) Catastrophies can seize your tongue in a stammer. When stuck with a vital message, untie tongue by: (1) Breathing deeply; (2) then breathe in quicker but exhale slowly and calmly; (3) Speak in a monotone, pitching voice higher (this is like singing – and singers never stammer in song); (4) Try humming the sound 'mmmm' in front of word you are trying to get out

Dust cloud
Stir sand or dust into column if chance of help approaches. And it is calm.

Signalling mirror
Most vital aid. An opened tin can substitutes. Punch 3mm (1/8 in) hole in centre of can top (this need not be taken completely off the can if you don't want to

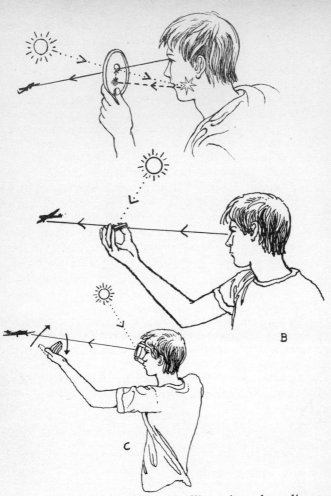

Fig 5   Three ways to hold a signalling mirror depending on position of the sun

remove it). Hold up to face and sight aeroplane below sun. The sunspot which falls on your cheek via the hole can then be bounced back through hole at aircraft so long as (i) you hold plane in sight (ii) tilt tin lid so that sunspot disappears into hole. Note: reflection must be on both sides of mirror for your face must be reflected on one side of the tin (so you can see the sunspot), and the sun must be reflected from the other side.

If aircraft is in a position away from the sun, the diagram shows how to bounce sunlight towards pilot using either of two different grips – B and C. (Using grip C the palm of the other hand acts as test-target to help direction of flash.)

Keep flashing even at empty view: flash could be seen kilometres/miles away by aircraft. Ease off if plane nears into intermittent flashes so as not to dazzle.

Bonfire

(*See also Too Cold page 147.*) Day and night use. If fuel scarce then hoard the material under stones, branches, leaves, soil, grass until a plane or ship passes. Then light quickly. Rock or log platform underneath fire helps. Keep petrol (if available) standing by to boost flames. Build more than one signal fire if possible. Keep checking them during bad weather. Kindling can be kept dry by body warmth.

Smoke signals

Has to be a calm day. Use (i) white smoke on clear days by adding moss, green foliage, sprinkling fire with urine (ii) black smoke for gloomy days by burning rubber (floormats/tyres), oil or oily rags. But first ensure you have a good fire which cannot be snuffed out easily.

Parachute-tepee

A kind of wigwam made from branches and parachute fabric (*see Too Cold page 145*). You can burn a fire inside to convert shelter into beacon – like electric bulb glowing through a lampshade.

Torch

Save battery torch until chance of rescue nears. Even small torch shows up well in open country at night. Keep it moving. Reflect circle of light on snow or bright reflector as well as pointing torch at sky or horizon.

Wave flaming spruce branch, or hanks of lit-up dried and knotted grass, or burning oily rags on stick.

Whole spruce tree makes excellent torch when ignited if (a) conspicuously placed (b) thick branched (c) you make a bird's nest of intertwined dead branches low down in the centre (d) you shield this with leaves, spare fabric, branches etc. until drone of plane is heard. If tree is snow-covered when you want to light-up, keep nest cover in place until you have shaken off snow. Petrol helps to light. Tips of spruce should flare . . . and show for miles.

Radio transmitter and other SOSs
Use immediately if intact, and while batteries are in working order, by sending distress signals at regular intervals. *Emergency transmitter* (when limited range save until possible help approaches). *Rockets* (keep dry until help near). *Sea marker dye* (good for staining snow too). *Gunshot* (save until help near). *Smoke flares* (save too).

Distress Signals

Letters SOS can be used anywhere: sounded, flashed, smoke puffed, written – even blinked. In morse code the letters become – 3 dots, 3 dashes, 3 dots. Pause then repeat.

Some other recognized distress signals are:

1. International Mountain Distress Signal: 6 flashes, whistles or waves in a minute, then a minute's silence, then repeat. Rescuing answer is 3 flashes, and whistles a minute, then a minute's silence, then repeat.
2. International Ground-Air Signals. (*Page 26.*) These should qualify the big SOS letters made in shadow writing on snow, sand, soil, grass, shale.
3. International Ground-Air Body Signals. (*Page 26.*)
4. Three fires in a triangle. If fuel is plentiful cover two fires until needed, and use third as camp fire.
5. On boats signals include: gunshot; flames (from tar or oil barrel say); a square flag with anything looking like a ball above or below it.
6. Red triangle (made, say, from sticks draped in red fabric) hanging from window. Also a road warning of traffic crash or breakdown ahead.
7. Stretching both arms up high while facing oncom-

ing trains – or, at night, swinging a light from side to side – signifies crisis to the driver.
8. In football stadium waving a white handkerchief is signal Red Cross/St Johns/St Andrews ambulance-men recognize.
9. Waved-high stethoscope tells rush-hour point duty traffic policeman that a doctor on emergency call needs priority.

Going For Help

When in a group and an accident has only injured one or some of party (say up mountain/in cave/on island) go for help when route is known/messengers are fit to travel/route for help is possible.

(Note: but only after all party is safe/injured have been given first-aid/made as warm as possible.)

Messengers going for help should:

1. **Be two in number if possible – always leaving one person with the injured.**
2. **Take written message giving**
   Location of injured (*as exactly as possible including preferably six-figure OS grid reference*)
   Injuries
   Time of accident
   Number in group
   Help needed
3. **Go quickly but safely to nearest habitation/ telephone.**
4. **Wait there for rescuers so they can guide back.**

SOS When You Don't Want Others to Know

Examples: 'Hey, Rube!' is code meaning 'Emergency!' in circuses (fire in big top/escaped lion/brawl); a coat lapel rubbed is the underworld sign police are about ('collar felt'); the bell on a bus sounded three times rapidly means bus conductor/inspector/mechanic is in trouble.

Answering an SOS

Let survivors know you've seen them. Always answer

Yes

N No

 Need compass and map

K Direct me way to go

 Am going this way

 All well

 Need signal lamp

 Will try take off

 Aircraft badly damaged

Not understood

I Need doctor

II Need first aid

 Need firearms

△ Probably safe to land here

X Unable to proceed

L Need fuel oil

W Need engineer

F Need food and water

Yes

Pick us up

All well

No

Our receiver is operator

Land here

Need mechanical aid. Long delay

Need doctor urgently

Can proceed shortly

Use drop message

Do not try to land

Fig 6   Ground-air signals

a distress call if you can help. If you cannot, raise the alarm and try to get help from those who can. It is essential you get the position of survivors – jotting it down on paper as soon as you see or hear SOS if in remote country. Or scratch it on slate, tree bark, metal.

It is better to try for extra help than try to attempt the impossible – if you can't help directly – which won't help at all. *Survival* means your own self-preservation comes first.

In a Tight Spot

You are never lonelier than when buried alive. (*See also Too Dark page 120.*)

Trapped among or by roof-fall, or in any circumstance where there may be a narrow avenue of escape – either to open-air or to a position where you can signal for rescue (through chink blowing air) – crawl, wriggle, squeeze or push through.

But if safe where you are and you are virtually sure of rescue *stay there*. Don't risk precipitating further rubble collapse. Only if *no* chance of rescue should tentative efforts be made to inch through.

Crawls and squeeze-throughs can be safe – say slots, slits and bedding planes in caves unaffected by a roof collapse and possibly offering an escape route when main corridor is blocked.

Such escape routes include porthole/manhole/skylight-squeezes.

Main principles are:

1. Strip off clothing so that if you are forced to back out it doesn't ruck up and cause jamming. Belts with large buckles are dangerous on same count.
2. Most likely person to succeed in wriggling through goes first, following – where possible – any draught of air or gleam of light.
3. If roof unstable wait until he gets through. Then follow, handling everything as if it were high explosive. When surrounds are solid, however, wriggle through with hands touching the feet of person in front.
4. A body stiff with tension is more likely to get stuck

than one relaxed. Experiment with body positions. Don't rush to get through. Big people can squeeze through amazingly small spaces so long as they relax. Empty lungs before trying tight bit.

5. Help a stuck person by 'talking' him through. Push and pull if physically possible and if captive relaxes.

6. Don't try to yank someone through hole by pulling on a rope, belt or sheet tied round his waist. Could jam him fast. Instead use a handline. First man through tows string of belts tied together with reef knots. He anchors this at far end. Anyone stuck can then pull themselves along hand over hand. Even so, this could lead to muscles tensing, and a jammed person would have to stop and relax to progress.

7. Probably best plan for helping wriggler in difficulty is a loop at the end of the string of belts. Stuck person works foot into loop and (a) bends at knee of that leg (b) helpers take in slack of line and anchor it (c) captive straightens leg squirming forward from its power, then flexes knee again (d) helpers pull in slack again . . . and so on.

8. Don't try sliding *down* a slope with arms out ahead – it is almost impossible to get back. Instead try one arm ahead at a time. Or tuck both beneath chest.

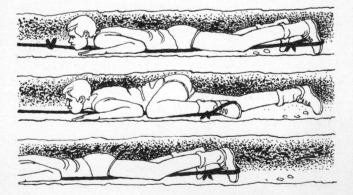

Fig 7 Tight spot footloop rescue

28

9. Where roof lifts a little, stoop with hands on knees. Or go on all fours, and crouch on haunches when resting. Or waddle along on haunches. This keeps knees off the ground.

   (It is possible to black-out through pain on kneecaps. They are not designed to carry the body. Body heat escapes through them on to cold floor. And crawling on knees over any distance is far too inefficient.)

   Ways of avoiding wriggling on knees: lie on outside of leg and hold up body on forearm. Trail other foot behind as you shove forward. Change over to other side for a rest. Or sit on a leg and squirm forward lifting lower thigh and buttock during each thrust.

10. Flat-out crawling and wriggling . . . tuck elbows into sides, hands under shoulders. Or grip fists under chin with elbows nudging solar plexus, and thrust forward with the toes (lift body and knees clear at each reptilian movement). It is not a good plan to reach forward all the time with both hands – for one thing, it usually means your body drags along the floor.

Child's head stuck between railings
Gently turn child upside down (two helpers best). Head is then eased out as easily as it went in. (Child is stuck because ears flatten as head goes in, but are forced outwards if head is pulled directly backwards.)

Load Handling

Survival situations call for lifting, pushing, carrying and manhandling at all ages and conditions. Try to avoid rupture or slipped disc risk by following these few simple principles.

Key rules:
Don't jerk, strain, tug wildly. Think, then p-u-s-h or l-i-f-t or c-a-r-r-y smoothly. Never hold your breath when load handling, but breathe freely. *Bend knees rather than your spine. Your back should never look like a question mark '?' but instead should emulate an 'I', or '/' or ')'. As upright as possible.*

Fig 8   Lifting

Lifting from the ground

Bend knees, crouching. Pull load – say a heavy rock –
on to your toes. This allows fingers to slide underneath. Lift rock on to knees, sliding forearms underneath. Stand up, back as straight as possible, legs
doing the work, lifting rock to chest. Curl fingers at far
side of rock.

Carrying

Can be done as you stand now: rock at chest height,
back straight. Alternative ways of carrying (depending on shape and type of load) are:

(a) On a shoulder. Keep changing sides to avoid
    straining.
(b) On hip. Rather cumbersome method. Useful
    when load too heavy to be lifted to shoulder.
(c) At pelvis level. Both arms straight down. Best if
    fingers can interlock below load. Carry loads short
    distances only this way.

Manoeuvring

Lifting and carrying long heavy loads like logs, posts,
bouncing cars out of ditch (*see Too Slow page 234*),
pieces of furniture.

1. Use lifting principles. Grip one end of long object at
   best point (bumpers on car/near ground under
   log/under edge of sideboard). Bend knees, and
   keep back as straight as possible.

30

2. Keep lifting, then relaxing to bounce cars.
3. Lift and walk crabwise with log, say, if on your own. Then lower that end (carefully, bending knees) and go to other end. Lift and carry this forward past the far end. Then lower and repeat with the other end.
4. Two men can manoeuvre a long object like this . . . each takes an end, and crouches, hands low at best gripping position. One gives commands – *Ready, Lift!* They lift together and walk crabwise rather than backwards or forwards.
5. Unwieldy rocks can be manoeuvred by lifting to one edge, then rolling (while you balance rock upright) for a few feet under own momentum. Take care it doesn't land on your toes.

Pushing
Drive from your *legs*. Arms can be outstretched with elbows 'locked', or completely bent. Back or shoulder against the object is probably best position.
(a) Place back to object, legs at 45 degrees to the ground. Bend knees, dig heels into ground, then straighten legs. Repeat.
(b) Face object and push with straight arms. These together with your body and legs should be in straight a line as possible. Lock elbows. Don't push upwards, but rather horizontally and forward. Steer the object (van say) by the push from your legs and angle of your shoulders and back.
(c) Bend both legs and press shoulder against object. Arms should be completely bent, but hands grip so that when you straighten legs the object moves forward (and upward at your end). Useful for object like crate which needs raising to swivel or slide into position.

Solo First Aid

Fantastic self-first-aid has been done by lone survivors. American pilot hacked off leg while swinging from parachute caught in jungle canopy. Trapper used hunting knife to cut/saw/sear gangrenous leg. Both survived.

People have always survived brutal surgery. British

31

Fig 9   Pushing

sailors once had legs amputated and stumps sealed
with pitch. Kit Carson took off a companion's arm
with waggon bolt, razor and saw – searing stump with
hot iron.

Women have given birth on the spot – alone. Men
have dragged smashed limbs/skulls/bodies for miles
. . . all should give you hope if ever similarly disabled.

If on your own when injured, but still conscious and
able to move and think, you may be able to carry out
the first-aid principles explained later relevant to each
section (like childbirth in *Too Crowded page 69*) – or
enough of them to pull through.

But one factor that could be fatal is present in *all*
first-aid situations – and the more you are aware of it
the more you may be able to combat it . . .

Shock

Many people have died after injury because of untreated shock.

Shock of the accident weakens the body. It lowers your vital activities. Shock increases under pain/exposure/exhaustion. It must always be treated in *all* survival situations.

Treatment
Act immediately – unless some more pressing need like severe bleeding. Or, if you are treating someone else, they stop breathing.

1. **Find shelter from rain/wind/snow (***see Too Cold page* **140). If conditions OK move as little as possible.**
2. **Lie down comfortably and slightly raise feet.**
3. **Loosen tight clothing without chilling.**
4. **Relieve pain if possible and treat injuries.**
5. **Get warm with extra clothing/covering, but don't make victim hot enough to cause sweating – don't overheat. Important – no hot water bottles.**
6. **Give nothing by mouth – allow a thirsty victim to such a moist cloth.**
   and if you are treating someone else for shock:
7. **Reassure patient.**
8. **Avoid noise and panic.**

Getting a Doctor

A telephone operator will always be able to help you with a list of available doctors whether you are in roadside call box/strange town/home (when no answer from your own doctor's number).

A hotel proprietor will contact a doctor for you.

Use 999 service for ambulance after accident.

If no telephone near, say after road crash, stop someone passing and ask them to phone urgently.

When phoning always say where you are as exactly as possible e.g. give nearest town/city/village, and any landmarks. Say, also, what help is needed – how many need it.

Too
Crowded

2 Too Crowded

Two is a crowd when one is booting/goring/biting the other. Suffused with pain, rage, hate and fear, your chances of surviving human or animal attack are unpredictable.

Crushed in crazed soccer crowd, throttled in emergency exit stampede or trampled in rush for lifeboats . . . mob force is as lethal as a charge of elephants/wolves/sharks. And much more likely.

What can someone unarmed and unversed in self-defence do when things get too crowded? So different is each individual, so varied are circumstances, the only hard and fast rule is hard and fast action when it comes to the crunch.

Recognize Danger

Escalating panic on jammed escalator; screams in discotheque; footsteps following you; dancehall punch-up. None of these – or any other trouble – need affect you directly. But be near them and you could be involved.

The human body *knowing* itself in danger is much stronger than one which doesn't (despite escapes in crises by the drunk/sleeping/unconscious). Aware in time and body pumps adrenalin into bloodstream as a tone booster/muscle accelerator/blood vessel constrictor. It can make all the difference between death and survival.

When trouble flares steel yourself. Expect it to spread and involve you. Take action.

Preparedness
1. **Fight down panic.**
2. **Avoid getting involved if at all possible.**
3. **Be looking for an escape route well in advance.**
4. **Try to sidestep trouble when face to face.**
5. **When trouble is head-on – resist with everything.**

Self-Preservation

Crushed in crowd
Aim to ride like buoy in rough sea – where tide is extremely powerful. To go under means drowning from suffocation and trampling. Brace like a powerful spring (as shown).

1. **Take deep breath.**
2. **Tense biceps/shoulders/back against pressure.**
3. **Bunch arms in front of stomach – possibly shielding child within.**
4. **Lift both feet off ground so they are not trampled on.**
5. **Keep moving wherever possible.**

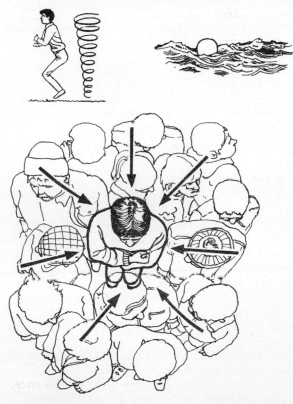

Fig 10   Spring and buoy position in surging crowd

At first signs of crowd-surge squirm away from anything solid like wall, barrier or pillar.

In hysterical/swaying/terrified crowd this is all you can do. Note: most vulnerable position of all is to be caught with hands in pockets. Neither should you clasp hands with interlocked fingers in front of body.

Where crowd is limited – too many trying to get out of emergency exit, say, try to calm panic by shouting humorous understatements.

Woman being followed
At sign of persistent footsteps behind . . .

1. *Walk faster*
   if footsteps still follow
2. *Run*
   if footsteps follow running
3. *Scream*
   if attacked give your resistance everything.

Screaming is often sufficient deterrent. But if not, fight like hell. The object is to stay alive, so don't use half-measures.

Think ahead when followed and choose some weapon to have in hand if grabbed, from whole arsenal you carry – from high heels to hat pins.

(a) Comb with teeth dragged across underneath nose.
(b) Umbrella stabbed forward.
(c) Matchbox held protruding from thumb side of fist – struck hard on assailant's temples.
(d) Nail file/hairpins/safety pins/fingernails/ballpoint pens/hairbrush handle – all useful jabbers and gougers.
(e) Key ring held in palm with keys sticking through slits between fingers.
(f) Face powder blown or hair spray sprayed into attacker's eyes.
(g) Coins slipped between fingers of clenched fist in advance.
(h) Handbag with hand wrist slipped through strap ready to swing as a club.
(i) To land blow more effectively with clenched fist punch at spot way beyond attacker's face/sternum/genitals. Do not tuck thumb inside fist.

If approached suddenly by a man, and no time for running – *talk*. And in meantime prepare defences as above. Say – looping hand through handbag strap.

Breaking grips

Use everything: belt knee hard into testicles; smash with foot under attacker's knee; drag foot down shin, and stamp on instep of attacker's foot; kick under kneecap.

Close-range kick with knee is best as it is harder for the protagonist to grab and pull you off-balance. But if you do kick from a distance (say against knife/bottle/razor attack) don't use orthodox football-type kick which can be seen coming for miles. Do it this way:

1. **Turn sideways on or backwards to attacker.**
2. **Lift knee high into stomach.**
3. **Shoot out leg horizontally behind, turning foot sideways (aim for knees/shin/crotch).**
4. **Pull back foot instantly after connecting.**

Ram with point of elbow; butt with head if in range; pry off fingers by wrenching them backwards – especially the little fingers; escape through the attacker's thumbs (*see page* 42); use persistent pressure with edge of little finger (palm flat, fingers together, thumb flexed outwards) under assailant's nose to break fierce grip (not necessarily on you.)

Stick fingers into attacker's eyes (1st and little finger, or 1st and 3rd fingers, of one hand make useful jabbing fork spaced just right for most eyeballs).

Distract attention *instantly* when attacked. Hanky/ashtray contents/spit can be aimed at attacker's face followed up by own attack. Or escape.

But be *quick* about it.

Arm from behind throttling you. If right arm is being used then attacker's right foot will probably be forward and just behind yours (and vice versa if left arm is used). Stamp hard on instep with heel.

Fingers strangling you from behind. Grab any of fingers and bend them backwards, then burst hands sideways away from your head.

Fig 11　Breaking stranglehold and bear-hug from behind

Strangled from the front.
(a) Grab any of fingers and bend/twist/wrench *quickly* backwards, separating his hands far apart, or
(b) Bring both of your arms (close together) up between opponent's hands viciously and outwards to cleave the grip. Note: do a shin-grinding and instep-stamping follow-up – one variation of retaliation.

Bear-hugged from front. Slap an arm up over outside one of attacker's arms *quickly*, cup his chin and snap his head back. Chuck knee up hard and stamp on instep when all else fails.

Body-hugged from behind. Pry his fingers back *instantly* before grip becomes concrete. Butting backwards with head can work if upper arms pinned – then grab for attacker's fingers (if set in consolidated grip try screwing knuckles into back of hand).

If lifted high from behind, dig heels hard back into crotch/thighs/shins – and run. But be ready for when suddenly dropped. Keep your balance.

Pushed in chest. Press both hands on top of hand pushing you, lean forward, step backwards and force down with bottom edges of your hands to lever him down.

Wrists (and lower arms) gripped. Escape through the thumbs which are weakest part (*Fig 12*). If your hands held up to protect face and wrists are grabbed – swing both arms down and outwards immediately, and disjoin his grip at the thumbs.

If your hands low and wrists or forearms gripped, then instantly wrench arms up and outwards, again putting pressure on opponent's thumbs.

But if two hands are gripping one of your wrists whip up your other hand between attacker's arms, close over fist of the imprisoned hand and wrench either up or down (and towards protagonist) depending whether your wrist being gripped is high or low.

Or, if circumstances allow, just hit attacker with other fist in face/solar plexus/stomach.

Being butted/kicked/punched. Try to sway/duck/dodge with body movement first . . . as trunk movement much quicker than arm reaction. Things happen so fast you are virtually defenceless, but:
(a) When lapels grabbed be ready for being butted in

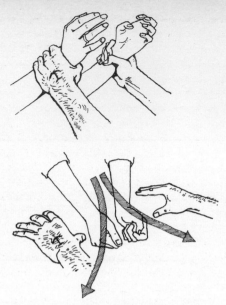

Fig 12   Escaping through thumbs

Fig 13   Kidney and head protection when booted

face by oncoming head. Your only defence is to get
in first by butting forward hard so top of your head
hits opponent on bridge of nose – hard.

(b) When lying on ground and being kicked try to
keep rolling, shielding parts being kicked with

arms. *But* always protect head as priority. Clasp base of skull with both hands, bring wrists across ears and side of head, and pressing elbows together. Bring knees up, crossing ankles to save genitals.

(c) In hand-to-hand brawl avoid lying on back, but pivot on hip to punch/kick/jab attacker with topmost leg and arm.

In all attacks it pays to shout/gasp/yell more than you need: feign pain. Especially when at receiving end (lying on ground and being kicked). Attacker may be satisfied sooner when you appear in agony.

Shout when attacking too. Expelling air makes you stronger/excited/intimidates.

When facing weapon

If no space to manoeuvre, no escape avenue, no inclination to get out – try to take weapon away (apart from a gun where you have to play it by ear – talk/divert attention if circumstances favourable/but usually acquiesce).

Person with gun could feel so upper-hand that he is careless. If absolutely essential you must escape (say

Fig 14   Thwarting underarm knife attack

you are being herded into van preparatory to be being thrown into Tyne in a sack) think of a rush attack. The corny old cowboy film trick of glancing over gunman's shoulder can still help you here. Do it subtly. Look of dawning recognition quickly stifled might make your captor start to look round.

But never rush a knife . . .

Keep attacker at distance. Use chair/spade/ice axe – anything solid and handy. Jab/stab/prod in defence rather than make roundhouse swings. Make sure assailant doesn't grab your defensive gear with his free hand. Tuck elbows into side and fingers into palms.

Wrap coat/rug/towel around a forearm to fend off attack with if nothing else.

Note how knife is held.

(a) If it is going to be thrown at you, attacker will usually have to change grips on it which gives you a moment's warning.

(b) Beware knife held underarm which is stabbed upwards and can slip through ribs easily and can mean expertise in attacker.

Fig 15   Combating overarm clubbing

44

(c) Knife stabbed down at you could be sign that assailant isn't real knife fighter (though not necessarily so) as harder for knife to enter ribs from above.

Ways of removing weapon differ tremendously. Three quick methods are shown which work so long as knife wrist can be caught quickly enough – the hard part.

Note: when all else fails – especially in drunken bottle-brawls – lash foot into genitals, but don't hesitate once you decide to kick. Best kick – turn your back and lash backwards like a horse. (*See page 39.*)

Such a kick gives you more reach than the man with the weapon – especially as your body leans back as counter balance. Aim hard at the knee. It can prove *very* effective.

Diagrams show the holds. When knife is coming upwards in attacker's right hand try to grab that wrist with your right hand and pull his arm across your body. At same time twist your body sharply to right so his elbow lies across your body. Belt your left arm across his chest to divorce him of knife (this can also snap his arm). (*See Fig 14.*)

Fig 16   Twisting and ducking to break knife grip

Knife striking down in attacker's right hand: try to catch that wrist with your left hand, then slot your right hand under his elbow and lock it on your *own* wrist. Force his arm back until he is forced to drop weapon (or have his arm broken). (*See Fig 15.*)

Another way is to catch knife-wrist and both hands (overhand-grip), twist your trunk hard left, duck under protagonist's armpit, yanking hard to break the knifehold. (*See Fig 16.*)

The Citizen's Arrest (unofficial)

If you catch a villain and have the manpower/girlpower/*power!* – detain him thus:

1. **Have him embrace a lamp post/flagpole/tree as if trying to climb it . . .**
2. **Right leg across left, toe of right shoe pushed behind lamp post.**
3. **Push thug down into sitting position.**

When police car arrives captive can be taken by arms and lifted. There's no other way (as left shoe binds right leg and right shoe binds lamp post).

Potential Attackers

Hijacker
Do exactly as told – neither staring in eye or making any sudden, unnecessary or menacing movements. (*See also When facing weapon page 43.*)

(If shot at from a distance in the open anything like a folded cape/policeman's serge coat/sheepskin held up loosely in front of you can sharply decelerate bullet and take sting out of it.) This is a drastic measure – when no other way.

Burglars
If you wake up in the night and discover a burglar . . .
    If in bed:

1. **Bite pillow corner and pretend to be asleep.**
2. **Inform police as quickly as possible.**

If he wakes you up:

1. **Ask what he wants.**

2. **Let him take money or property.**
3. **Do not provoke or anger. Keep quiet.**
4. **Try to remember what he looks like.**
5. **Contact police when you can.**

If you surprise a burglar:

1. **Avoid giving any aggressive impression. It is safer for many to pretend to faint.**

If you only suspect someone is in your home:

1. **Keep the lights on. A light-out situation gives an intruder the advantage.**
2. **Call police as soon as possible. Burglars usually look for an easy touch – not trouble.**

Hitchhiker who pulls weapon

Golden rule is: never pick up hitchhikers.

If you do and worst happens try to do *something* – what depends on circumstances. If you haven't chance to act quickly when customer turns nasty, acquiesce and drive on. But be thinking of best action. Remember drivers who did nothing and were left shot or stabbed at the wheel. And you have whip hand as driver.

Things that have worked:

(a) Managing to pass on SOS at filling station – possibly when gunman has 'hostage' (your front seat passenger) but lets you get out.
(b) Crossing double white lines in front of police car – also misbehaving in other ways; and flashing lights at patrol car, etc.
(c) Surreptitiously pulling out choke, explaining jerky engine as serious petrol pump/carburettor/electrics trouble which needs attention – and once out of car *run* (if assailant has gun run in zig-zags to nearest cover.)
(d) Feigning sickness: diabetic insulin-surplus/heart trouble/appendicitis while clutching body/slump over wheel/pull into side. Then either overpower and thump or get out and run.

Remember here your elbow is strongest weapon available when struck into passenger's floating ribs (just above waist). Some other pretext may give you opening to strike thus – say extending arm as if to adjust choke/ashtray/wipe windscreen.

(e) With front seat hitchhiker holding gun/knife/razor on you, consider stopping very, very abruptly if you are wearing seat belt and he is not. And eject him into dash/scuttle/windscreen.

(f) If a good enough driver, give unwanted passenger very fast drive so he knows that to kill or injure you while at wheel will mean horrifying crash.

If driving with valuable load and stopped by someone who suggests you get out to attend to flat tyre/unsafe load/lights out/an accident ahead – don't leave your vehicle. Drive on until sure you are safe then check.

Waved-down by police (and with valuable load) don't leave vehicle if asked – but offer to drive to nearest police station. Bogus police and warrant cards hard to detect from real thing at night.

Driver who kidnaps hitchhiker

Put on spewing/puking/vomiting act all over car interior. You may manage real thing if you stick two fingers down your throat. If car stops get out and run.

See also Too Fast page 215 (when driver is drunk/ suicidal/tearaway).

Pickpockets and bag snatchers

Thieves who depend on stealth are unlikely to be dangerous – unless you catch them red-handed and try to retaliate. Likely situations: in crowds thronging racecourses/prizefights/subway trains and rush-hour streets.

Pickpockets will always try to distract you just before they have a chance. Be ready for such a moment. When somebody knocks the parcel out of your hand, say, and hands it back with profuse apologies. And keep your other hand on your money. Keep walking.

Safest place for a man's money: the two front trouser pockets as they are near a sensitive area. *Never* use the back hip pocket.

Safest place for a woman's money: a purse inside her handbag which should be tucked firmly under her arm – not dangling from a shoulder strap.

Peeping Tom
Don't attack – he might be in shouting distance of other kinky characters who 'patrol' lovers' lanes/parks/laybys after closing time.

If in car parked in field/lane/copse and face looms at window – keep inside. Doors should be locked and windows wound-up. Don't open window to anyone who taps on it – could admit a gun (viz. A6 murder).

Fact the spy-er has been seen is enough usually to make him sheer off. In any case – drive off yourself.

If in building with telephone – dial 999.

Don't rush into the attack in face of such complete unknown.

Fighting drunk
Humour.

If involved in brawl, drunks can offer astoundingly strong grip. Hit hard in stomach and this may make him sick.

Madman
Humour (again can have three times the strength of normal person).

Furious driver
Avoid being pulled from your car seat and battered by motorist/lorry driver/cabbie who is incensed at way you cut in front of him and catches you at traffic lights.

Lock doors and refuse to get out.

If driving door is forced open, back out through other front door.

Or jump out towards complainant – fast. Don't sit there as sitting target for a punch on the nose. Or possibly worse.

Holding two fingers with the thumb cocked (as if shooting yourself) as an apology, or talking, can often get you out of this spot – but be ready.

Mob
Can vary from a small crowd of Continentals angered by your hitting pedestrian/car/dustcart with your vehicle while on holiday to lynching party out for blood.

Get away – escape in time.

If not: backs to the wall.

If you can dispatch the first assailant to lay hands on you summarily enough, the others *may* have second thoughts about coming to grips with you.

Drowning person

Keep well away as drowning people have strong fighting instinct (*see Too Wet page 101*). Break holds as previous if grabbed by drowner (say following shipwreck).

Natives

If attacked take cover. Avoid fighting back unless poisoned darts (you suspect) are showering at you. And then fire *above* heads. Killing primitive tribesman will really precipitate things.

When you feel you are being watched in jungle stand in any clearing, show yourself empty-handed in all directions. If still not sure, leave gifts in obvious place and come back to check if still there.

On meeting natives . . . show yourself unarmed by holding out arms and hands. Use sign language to show your needs, and you may be taken to village.

(a) Play it by ear. Take things slowly. Show yourself friendly/well-intentioned/non-scared. Smile.

(b) Aim to see headman. Ask him for any help you need. Sign language will get through. Don't demand. Give gifts.

(c) Don't be too generous in handing out possessions/ coins (not paper money)/food as payment. It is unwise to overpay. Be fair – try to win their confidence. Keep promises.

(d) Respect customs – and native homes/women/ possessions. If you don't leave them alone expect the worst. Survival when tribesmen are not sure about you is very much a case of doing as you would be done by.

(e) Mix. Join in. Be prepared to become butt of their humour. Try to learn their tongue. Don't keep repeating faux pas which are obviously causing consternation.

(f) Learn what you can of locale, food and water supplies. Also whereabouts of hostile natives, anything that can help.

(g) Watch your possessions aren't pinched. Avoid living in native shelters (you could catch disease) if at all possible, but build your own, possibly with native help. Boil your water, prepare your own food – but don't make your segregation (for health reasons) obvious.

While they are tying you up

Whether natives strapping you to a stake or assailant who breaks into house while you are watching TV and binds you to a chair . . . knowing basic escapology is a must (you don't have to be a Houdini to get away).

1. **Arms to body.** Take deep breath. Pull shoulders back. Flex arms against the bonds. Try to fold arms by simulating pain under the armpits so crossing arms while pretending to rub sore parts – then hook up as much slack as possible with 2nd finger (longest) while binder is unsighted on the blind side and/or underneath armpits.

   Let breath out, shoulders slump forwards and arms press into body – and bonds should slacken as you go smaller.

2. **Wrists and hands.** Brace these against the bonds, arched slightly. When keeping wrists apart press on fingertips and vice versa. *Push* against bonds, especially at point where they are being bound, using this contra-pressure. Try to keep hands in front rather than having them bound behind you.

   Free by relaxing hands and wrists and working until slack can ride over palms and fingertips – helped by long 2nd fingers which can feed loose loops over hands. Use teeth if knots in suitable position. Or work knot loose on some projection.

3. **Legs and ankles.** Flex thighs, knees, calves and ankles against the bonds. When bound at ankles brace shoe toes and knees together, forcing ankles apart. Keep feet (at toes) together and arch legs apart when thighs and calves are being bound.

   Free by relaxing legs. It is possible to free ankles,

51

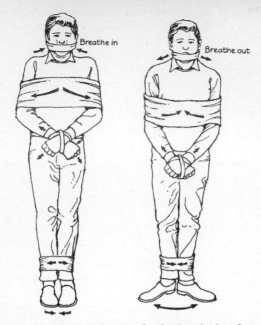

Fig 17   Bracing against and relaxing in bonds and gag

even though wrists still tied, if feet curled up behind and knot is in suitable place.

4. **Gag.** Tuck chin well in/clench teeth/puff out cheeks
   before they gag you. Try to free by rubbing face
   against wall, piece of furniture, anything projecting.
5. **If they tie you to tree, fence post, chair.** Same
   principles apply. Brace where possible against
   bonds, forcing part of body being bound away from
   object no matter how slightly by pressure against
   object elsewhere – e.g. being bound by shoulders to
   tree force back away from tree by pressing with
   calves at bottom of tree.

Note: irregular surfaces like trees present good
chances of escape as working bonds towards any
depressions in tree means more slack.

Remember . . . even 13 mm (½ in) slack in bonds
can mean escape using these principles. Usually you

can obtain more by determining your captors shall not do exactly as they want with you, and bracing against the rope/electric flex/wire.

A long rope bound round and round you gives better chance of escape than several short ropes at different points – ankles, wrists, chest and arms. When you see bonds overlapping realize you have chance of working slack.

Another resort: *fray* bonds on any sharp projection – rope is easier to saw through than cord.

Creatures from Outer Space (stepping from flying saucer)

There is no scientific evidence that aliens exist in the neighbourbood of earth. There are tens of thousands of unidentified flying objects. So far not one has been identified as a flying saucer.

Whether or not sighting aliens disembarking is merely an hallucination (most likely explanation) the safest course is to *get away*.

Animal and Aquatic Hazards

Animal attack is unpredictable.

You can expect it when hunting/trapping/cine-filming big game, but mostly fear lies in the mind of survivor in wilderness country. He could well escape without ever seeing a dangerous animal, and those he does – will often avoid him.

Animal kingdom does offer real danger, however – when cornered/surprised/with young. Some need no provocation.

Animal hazard is not only present in jungle, but in many places – parks/reservations/fields/mountains/streets/sea. And on the beach . . .

Donkeys

Seaside resorts treat for donkey bites each year. Dissuade children from offering titbits to donkeys. But if they must – offer sweets/carrot chunks on *flat of hand*. *Remedy – see page 66.*

Weever fish

UK's only poisonous fish, weevers burrow into sand,

their venous dorsal fins sticking up. These sting like an adder bite. *Remedy – see page 66*.

Stingray
Looking like a skate, the stingray is an unwelcome visitor to UK waters. It has a long flexible tail with sharp spine – used as a weapon. Effect: similar to weever fish. *Remedy – see page 66*.

Portuguese Man O'War
This jelly-fish resembles a blue or pink plastic bag floating in shallows or rock pools. It makes rare appearances along UK shores. It trails 13m (40ft) long sting with venom like a cobra. The aged or very young can die. Avoid. *Remedy – see page 66*.

Bulls
Keep your eye on the bull. Biggest cause of fatalities and injuries is carelessness/familiarity/contempt. Bulls are completely unpredictable.

If you have to go in field with bull, keep to edges. Otherwise detour outside the field – some bulls may take no notice of intruders some of the time, then attack. They can run and swerve faster than humans. Ways to evade . . .

(a) Try not to turn your back to a bull unless near wall/fence/tree to which you can sprint. If some way to go, however, try to dodge – still backing away. Never square up to a bull.

It can help to slip coat/sweater/shirt off and toss aside before making final safety dash. And if bull is still some way off.

(b) Bulls tend to go for any bright colours – not necessarily red. Subdue anything bright as best you can.

(c) Bulls don't take to water easily – another escape avenue: river/lake outlet/canal.

(d) If with family (inconceivable if you have not been careless) draw off bull while women and children run in different directions – by flinging coat. Even then no knowing what bull will do and whom he will chase.

Fig 18   Bull evasion

(e) If thrown by bull only way to hurt him is by grasping the nose ring (if there is one) and hanging on with fingers.

(f) Another survival method that has worked is: feign death if you have already survived being thrown/gored/knelt-on.

Dogs

Ordinary village dog in other countries is dangerous. Semi-starved and savage, its bite can be fatal if dog has rabies. Signs – glazed eyes/foaming mouth/staggering.

Stone them to keep at bay if they attack you.

With other large dogs try not to give any aggressive impression.

(a) Stand your ground, calling *Leave!* and talking to dog quietly.

(b) If possible catch neck ruff and gently manhandle dog backwards to gate/door/barrier which can be slammed.

(c) Never grasp the tail (dog can whip round and bite).

(d) Push back towards rear of dog's mouth if it bites rather than tearing limb away. This can weaken grip and cause a less laccrated wound.

Wolves

Wolves are only *related* to dogs. Spinal anatomy is similar, but wolf has protective ruff and its spinal (cervical) vertebrae are thickly encased in neck muscle. Vulnerable parts: nose, lower ribs at side. Wolves are tearers, pack hunters usually, and hunters of weak victims, going after limbs. If attacked by a wolf:

1. Chop it on nose.
2. Slam arm to back of jaws.
3. If you go down with it, clutch its back in crossed legs.
4. Squeeze like hell with legs and cause a reflex backs-quirm, then try jerking hand on neck.

If bitten *see page 66*.

Bears

A hazard all over world (from Arctic to Yellowstone Park in America). Don't encourage 'tame' bears to approach you with food/posed-photographs-with-people-included/fooling about. They can maul without warning. Observe warning notices in such areas.

Marauding polar bear prowling round forced-camp should be shot: hard and dangerous to kill, yet relentless in its curiosity. Aim for neck/heart/throat shots just behind shoulder. One marksman on own very vulnerable.

Grizzly bears are dangerous (tan colour with blond collar and neck hump). Black and brown bears are generally less lethal.

Worth remembering: a bear runs faster uphill than down as front legs are shorter than rear.

Tigers

All big cats can either sheer away or attack. Unarmed survivors who have been face to face with tigers/ leopards/lions have used various methods: freezing still; staring back hard; yelling and screaming.

Snakes

In snake-prone country make lots of noise so as not to surprise – cause of most snake bites. Wear boots. Reinforce thin footwear with layers of cloth. Wind round ankles (but not too tight). Thrash with stick ahead when stepping over logs/rocks/thickets. Snakes are nocturnal – take torch and thick stick at night. Don't sleep on ground. Watch where you put bare hands.

If bitten, try to kill snake (with rock/stick/gun) – if you or companions have presence of mind among ensuing alarm. When sure it is dead handle by tail and take to doctor/hospital/sick bay in camp (kind of snake means venom can be identified).

Snakes will usually avoid you. Only 200 are fatally poisonous out of over 2,000 different kinds. Even poisonous snakes don't always inject lethal venom. A good chance you won't die if bitten. Adder is only poisonous snake in British Isles (not usually fatal in an adult).

See page 66 for treatment.

Spiders

Avoid by not rooting/groping/feeling under rocks, logs and in holes with your hands in potential spider country – whether in home-docked banana boat or abroad.

Black Widow (with reddish hourglass marking underneath) has most dangerous nerve poison which can kill. Tarantula is relatively harmless by comparison. Spiders don't often kill – but inflict pain.

Hairy spiders cause intense skin irritation if they touch you.

Scorpions

Be wary. They lie in dark places: don't disturb with bare hands when working among tree trunks/logs/

rocks/sand. Knock shoes/socks/clothing before dressing. Check bedding before you lie on it.

Poison affects nerve system, makes you vomit and can kill – especially children. Smaller scorpions are more potent than big ones. The poison glands are in tail and big claws.

Centipedes

Check clothing and bedding in hot climates. Nocturnal. If you feel one crawling over you in night – let it. Don't attempt to brush off. Very painful sting.

Insects

Disease (like malaria and yellow fever from mosquitoes) is biggest fatality risk. Cover up at all costs against swarms of flies.

(a) Cover face/extremities/upper body with mud.

(b) Improvise wide-brimmed hat.

(c) Improvise head net from shirt/T-shirt (sleeves pulled up through buttoned-up neckhole) worn round and over head and tucked into collar.

(d) Wear two layers of clothing where possible. Tuck trousers into socks/boots/puttees (made from cloth wound round and round spirally upwards from ankle to knees). Tie off bottom of trousers inside footgear with laces/string/vines. Tuck sleeves into gloves (makeshift ones: socks).

(e) Keep clothes on at night. Improvise mosquito net round bedding from any cloth.

(d) Use first-aid ointment/repellant/anti-malaria tablets if available. DEET (M-N-diethylmetatoluamide) is ultimate insect repellent (Repel 100, for instance, contains it in 95% concentration).

Pitching camp on right site is important. Steer clear of (1) swamps/pools/bogs (2) low-lying, damp and calm land (3) sheltered site. Instead choose high windy situation where possible.

Insect-proof shelter as tightly as materials allow – say with parachute canopy, or clothing. Cigarette smoke is a deterrent inside, but smoky fire better.

Light healthy fire outside, then add damp foliage/ferns/moss until smoking heavily. A smaller section of this is carried into back of shelter. Fan smoke (along with flies) back out through door.

Ants
Avoid anthills and antpaths. Beware when climbing tropical trees as ants which bite live high as well as ground-level. Look where you sit and sleep. Don't scatter food remains around – bury them.

Faced with remorseless march of ant army – just move your gear out of the path which will keep in a straight line (but do it in time).

Bees, Wasps, Hornets
If you disturb a nest (usually 3m–9m/10–30 ft up trees) and you are some metres/yards away sit tight for several minutes, then crawl away (wasps chase moving targets). If attacked run through thickest undergrowth or take to water.

Ticks
Strip off clothes often – especially in grassy areas. You may find ticks/leeches/bed bugs – among others. Examine each other. Ticks can be removed by brushing/flicking/tapping. But if head is attached under skin relax its grip with iodine/meths/lit-cigarette-held-near. Don't pull body, or head remains in and festers.

Leeches respond to flicking/salt/cigarette end, (they will get through any clothing). Don't pull if already attached to you.

Fleas burrowing under toe nails (or skin) to lay eggs may generally be removed with fire-sterilized knife/needle/pricker. And iodine applied.

There are many other parasites which can burrow below skin, fleas which can bite and insects which can fill you with disease.

In all pest-prone areas . . .
(a) Keep clothes on as barrier (with layers tucked in).
(b) Keep clothing dry as possible, clean and mended. Especially socks and stockings. Wash a lot.
(c) Never walk barefooted.
(d) If you fall into tropical water, no matter how fresh-looking, act: wring clothing; drain shoes;

towel-down all over; change into dry clothes if possible.
(e) Keep out of water unless forced to wade, as tremendous variety of attackers from waterborne-skin-burrowing worms to sting rays; jellyfish to barracuda; water snakes to electric eels; Portuguese Man O'War to coral reef stingers.

Crocodiles and alligators
They can lie with eyes just above water like logs. Or on banks.

Beware when wading across rivers, swimming or rafting across bays and estuaries in tropics. Don't thrash/splash/shout. Skirt well clear of any such infested water. If attacked get to side *fast*. Check thoroughly first before entering any deep water. Don't trust method of throwing stones to scare off crocodiles.

Sharks
Keep quiet in raft. Paddle away from blood/vomit/fish remnants/excrement floating on water. Avoid fishing near sharks. Wear dark clothing if possible and cover bare limbs as white-flash can attract them.

Don't jump overboard to swim from small boats without checking all round and underneath. Stay near boat. Avoid dangling hands or feet over side. Sharks come scavenging round craft without warning. If investigated be ready for craft to be nudged/scraped/bumped by shark. Avoid flashing bright objects to attract them even more. Keep quiet. Chances are they might lose interest if no apparent chance of food and swim on.

When attacked by shark and you are on raft: all face out back to back (tie yourselves together if rough sea) and kick out at shark; use knife in gills or eyes; jab snout/gills/eye with oar by prodding/stabbing/jabbing – not swinging.

If anyone dies throw body over at night and paddle fast away. Pull anyone injured into raft and treat for bleeding and shock (see later).

Gunshot can scare.

Use shark repellent if available.

Swimmers in shark infested waters should use regular smooth strokes. Panicky splashing movements attract the big fish. Also – stay clear of large schools of fish (another shark attraction).

Survivors in water without raft facing shark (or any dangerous fish like barracuda and swordfish) should form a circle facing outward and beat the water with powerful regular strokes. Float if you see triangular fin and shark doesn't seem to have spotted you.

Swimmer can try these measures when single shark attacks.

(a) Don't turn and flee but face and swim to one side as he comes in.

(b) Suddenly swim *at* shark.

(c) At close quarters – try kicking/punching/handing-off.

(d) Scream underwater.

(e) Slap surface water with hands.

(f) If armed – stab gills or eye.

Swans

Avoid – especially if you have dog and swan has cygnets. Large, angry swans have bone-breaking potential with wings like iron bars.

Crowd Hazards

Crowd risks run gamut from apoplectic argument which results in heart attack to bite of snake/punch of fist/kick of boot. Or emergency birth of baby.

Sprains, strains, splinters, cuts and bruises and other injuries are best treated cold first, heat later. Cold water/wet towel/ice pack applied first relieves pain and relaxes muscles.

Warm water/hot compress/hot water bottle used after inflammation subsides helps relieve pain and boosts blood circulation to injured part. Used too soon following injury, however, can be harmful.

Try to resist drinking/offering/carrying-alcohol in survival situations. It causes blood sugar shortage and drop in body temperature. If, however, you

must carry a hip flask at least take it with sugar/
glucose sweets/sugary food.

Shock
Always treat – as in all hazards (*see Too Lonely page 33*).

Bleeding
Priority hazard of all – even to non-breathing (*see Too
Wet page 105*).

Act *fast* when someone is losing lifeblood.

A little blood looks a lot. But blood is antiseptic and
will usually clot itself – so long as flow is slowed. Can
take a few seconds to over 10 minutes.

1. **Press directly with fingers (unless steel/rock/wood
   embedded).**
2. **Press on pad (hanky) to make blood stop or ooze.**
3. **Raise bleeding part of body.**
4. **Get to doctor/hospital fast.**
   > *Don't wash wound*
   > *Don't peel off blood clot*
   > *Don't use tourniquet or bandage too tightly*
   > *Don't take off pad – add more on top if bleeding
   > through.*
   > *Don't let pads move – bandage firmly with
   > tie/belt/stocking.*

Clean pad is not essential though preferable. Don't
mess round looking for hygienic one. Use handiest to
check spurting blood.

Forget about looking for special pressure points
(easily forgotten in crisis). Pinch wound edges
together with fingers. Keep pressing no matter how
exhausted/bloody/scared stiff you are.

Remember: raising a bleeding limb will force blood
to run uphill and slow down bleeding rate. Do that.

Bleeding inside victim
Happens in violent accidents – falling/crashing/
crushing.

Injured is cold/clammy/pale. Pulse is weak and
faint. Pain. Restlessness. Eyesight goes dim. Thirst
grows.

Frothy-red or coffee-grounds-like blood is spewed

up sometimes. Bowel movement can look like tar or be stained crimson.

Play safe. Don't give drinks (wet lips with sodden cloth). Move as little as possible. Get medical aid.

Unconsciousness

Test by touching eyeball gently – a blink = injured is conscious.

Never shout/shake/pummel. Don't try to force down fluids (and never try to give alcohol). If back does not appear broken (*see Too Fast page 226*) . . .

1. **Turn body and head to one side.**
2. **Clear mouth of dentures/vomit/dirt and check breathing.**
3. **Look for bleeding and stop.**
4. **Loosen clothing and treat for injuries.**
5. **Search pockets for identity – and notice of diabetes etc.**

Get stretcher/medical help/ambulance.

Fractured bones

Can range from break under unbroken skin to smashed bone ends rammed into each other. Sometimes bones stick into view, sometimes into internal organs.

Signs (if not obvious): *pain*, shock, power-loss of limb, swelling (compare one leg, say, with the other for size).

Never – unless going to be in wilds for ages – try to fix fracture back into place. Survivors in way-out situations have tractioned breaks on their own (like single man who hooks ankle of broken leg into fork of tree and pulls to reset leg straight). Normal situations need opposite of this treatment.

Leave broken bones alone as much as possible until they can be properly treated by doctor or hospital.

More danger from doing too much than too little.

Eliminate pain: this is best you can do. If your treatment does this, no matter how little or rough and ready, you are doing a good job. Elevate limb if possible – as fracture nearly always bleeds inside.

If injured crying out in pain, or *has* to be moved . . .

don't jab/prod/finger bones sticking into view. Stop bleeding. Ease limb into most comfy position. Splint to support a break with rolled-up newspapers/magazines/sticks – anything handy. And pad softly with rags/clothes/leaves (never use metal in cold climate).

Tie firmly with makedo bandages –ties/belts/cloth strips. And realize body makes best splint – arm to body; leg to leg; jaw to jaw – and so on.

Don't splint if possible. Wait for help.

Fractured skull (*see page 69*), broken spine (*see Too Fast page 226*), smashed pelvis . . . all asking for horrible trouble if you try moving unless absolutely necessary – and you know the score.

Wounds

Slit/cut/rip any clothing carefully (so it can be sewn up again if necessary). Be meticulous about *not* touching wound with fingers/having dirty hands/rubbing muck into sore. (*See also Potassium Permanganate page 154.*)

Sterilize tip of knife or needle with several matches before poking out foreign objects with point. Ice cubes anaesthetize skin.

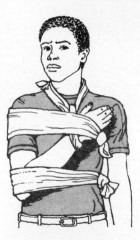

Fig 19   Bandages and padding to immobilize broken limb using body as splint

Wash round wound with soap and water (always smoothing away from edge of wound, never towards it). Don't pour iodine into the wound, though it can be used to clean surrounding skin (let it dry in air before dressing).

Swabbing wound with clean cloths and soap and water okay when surrounding edges been cleaned.

Be scrupulously clean.

When wound punctured by nail/knife/stabber squeeze wound to press out blood – and help cleanse.

Apply as clean a dressing as possible – not too tight. Doctor needed: don't forget lockjaw risk.

An ice cube held to cut helps stop bleeding (cold restricts blood vessels under skin).

Dislocation
Wrenched/twisted/all-to-cock bone at joint. Unusual shape tells of dislocation. Pain/power-loss/stiffness.

1. **Don't try to twist back into place.**
2. **Support in most comfortable position (pad where necessary).**
3. **Forget about splints.**

Sprains
Bruised swelling after wrist or ankle been in impact.

1. **Rest/immobilize/elevate.**
2. **Apply wet cloths.**

Wrist: make a simple sling to support arm against body.

Ankle: wrap round bandage in firm figure-of-eight round ankle and foot.

If swelling grows, untie, rewet and retie.

Chemical burns
(*See Too Hot page 171.*)

Black eye
Apply wet cloths or ice pack.

Human bites
Dangerous. Warrant a doctor. Swill immediately with running water.

Snake bite

Rare death. Skip those old heroics where trusty companion slashes bite site with knife and sucks out venom. Someone kill snake if possible.

1. Don't panic and rush/flap/run round.
2. Tell victim to lie dead still.
3. Apply firm bandage on heart side of bite (loosen it for one minute every half hour).
4. Wash (not rub) surface of bite with water.
5. Treat for shock and give no drinks.
6. Carry to doctor/hospital (with dead snake to identify poison if possible) urgently.

Dog bite

1. Wash well with soapy water.
2. But wash saliva well away from wound.
3. Cover with dry clean dressing.
4. Keep part immobile (splint).

Get patient to hospital.

Donkey bite

Potentially dangerous. Give fast, soapy wash. Apply clean dry dressing – and see doctor.

Weever fish

Standing on a fish barefoot burns. And can cause delerium. Weevers are not fatal (though foot may swell). Hospitals, reached quickly enough, have a pain-killing injection.

Stingray

Similar to weever fish.

Portuguese Man O'War

If stung – don't flap (it stimulates circulation). Stay still. Call for help. Ask someone to phone. Though it feels like a bad electric shock it is not usually fatal.

Fox/rat/bat/bites

More chance of rabies from these in Britain than from dogs. Get bite under running water and wash well with soap. Then dress.

Ant/mosquito bites
Ease pain with baking soda+water paste. Cover with
wet cloth when swelling.

Bee/wasp sting
Try to get sting out with tweezers or by prying carefully with flame – sterilized tip of needle or knife. Run
cold water over. Piece of soap comforts bee sting;
vinegar or lemon wasp sting.

Best pain-reliever: moisten sting area and rub
enough soluble aspirin on to leave a coating. If pain
returns, wetting aspirin coating again will help relieve
it.

When swarm has stung in mass of stings soak in
bath with baking soda stirred in (cool).

Insect in ear
Tip head towards sun/bulb/candle flame so insect is
drawn by light. Avoid poking.

Heart attack
Symptoms: sudden clutching bar/desk/side. Short-
ness of breath; pain in upper abdomen or chest (with
pains shooting down arms or up into neck and head);
coughing up pink froth (perhaps).

Doctor *quick*.

Meanwhile . . .

1. **Get injured as comfortable as can be (often semi-
   lying down).**
2. **Loosen clothing.**
3. **Cover patient (but don't overheat).**
4. **Don't carry or give drink.**
5. **Tell to breathe deeply, slowly, blowing out
   through mouth.**

Give kiss of life (*see Too Wet page 105*) if breathing
stops.

Choking
Called 'cafe coronary' because it looks similar to a
heart attack, chokers on small pieces of food cannot
speak/clutch throat/turn blue/collapse.

There are three solutions: (1) if victim coughs let
them get on with it (they're making their own survival

efforts); (2) if they cannot cough or speak – slap hard four times with heel of hand between shoulder blades (keeping their head low); (3) as a last resort quickly try abdominal pressure detailed as follows.

If sitting or standing:

1. **Stand behind and wrap arms round waist (and around chair if in chair).**
2. **Place thumb side of fist slightly above navel and under rib cage.**
3. **Grasp fist with other hand and press it into victim's abdomen with quick upward thrust.**
4. **Repeat if necessary.**
5. **After food is dislodged, get them to doctor.**

When collapsed and cannot be lifted:

1. **Lay on back.**
2. **Face them and kneel down astride hips.**
3. **With one hand on top of other, place heel of lower hand on abdomen slightly above navel and under rib cage.**
4. **Press into rib cage with quick upward movements. Repeat.**
5. **If they vomit, quickly turn on side and clear mouth with finger to prevent drawing of vomit into throat.**
6. **Get to doctor.**

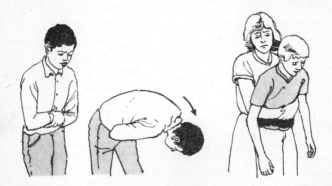

Fig 20   Action when choking (after trying backslaps on someone else to no avail)

68

Head injury
Violent blow (in car crash/boot-in melee/drunken fall) on skull could = dazedness/coma/bleeding from mouth, ears, nose. Headache, odd eye pupils.

Lie injured down. Cover up. Never let them struggle up and stagger about. If spine not broken (*see Too Fast page 226*) and face is flushed raise head on folded jacket/coat/sweater. If pale do not raise head.

Turn body and head gently to one side (if no broken back suspected) so blood/mucous/vomit drains out. Fit light clean dressing on head if bleeding (don't bind hard to force bones into brain).

Remember – the aim is to lie quietly (even if conscious) until medical help at hand.

Emergency childbirth
Happens anytime. Don't panic. Not unique situation. Let Nature handle it with you helping it along.

Above all . . .

1. **Don't pull baby/its cord/afterbirth attached to other end of cord.**
2. **Tie cord as soon as baby is delivered.**
3. **Cut cord only if no help likely. If help on way, tie cord but leave afterbirth attached.**
4. **Keep baby warm: place between mother's legs.**

Signs are: uterus starting to contract inside each half hour (very roughly). When pint of water pours out things really moving.

Preparation: lie mother-to-be on something flat, and spread with clean sheet/newspapers/plastic. Have hot water at hand if possible. Wash hands carefully. Wear hanky over mouth when helping. No messing – be clean. Give loads of encouragement.

Boil scissors well first. Get three lengths of string each about a handspan's length (just over) for cord tying.

Put mother in best position – on back, knees up – when bulge appears and birth imminent. Knees up, back near edge of delivery table.

(If mother-to-be is not too weak, squatting rather than lying down can be better position for delivery of baby and placenta.)

If bowels move wipe clean towards spine, away from birth route.

As birth happens tell mother to pant and not bear down. Baby's head/bottom/foot/arm could come first – don't pull, but feed it out. Only interfere if membrane is over baby's face (tear it). Or if cord is round baby's neck (ease/loop/slide it free). If head comes last and sticks pull gently 3 minutes after shoulders have come.

Be gentle. If cord is mistreated baby might bleed to death.

Lay baby (frog-slippery – don't drop) between mother's legs, cord not stretched, head downhill. And care for it thus:

(a) Bind ankles with cloth.
(b) Hook your fingers under binding and hang upside down. Let fluids drain from mouth and nose after opening mouth and holding head back a bit.
(c) Wipe face and mouth very gently with clean piece of cloth.
(d) When baby cries, put it immediately to mother's breast (she can always wean it later.) This helps mother feel better/helps stop uterine bleeding/keeps baby warm and happy. Also early fluid from breast contains vital nutrients for baby.
(e) If no crying nor gurgling/bubbling/breathing don't smack or forget and handle abrasively: give a very gentle kiss of life in about two minutes.

Ten minutes later (approx.) afterbirth will come, mother separating her legs and helping it out. (Note: bleeding can be checked often by gently massaging under the navel. Keep afterbirth intact in some container.)

If medical help is distant let blood run out of cord *into baby* before tying the cord. (Hospitals hold baby below level of mother's body until cord changes colour from blue to white.)

Bathe mother. Give her hot drinks. Treat for shock. Congratulate. Reassure. Keep check on breathing/pulse. Let her sleep.

Too
Dry

3　Too Dry

Thirst bursts through every human need. Owed water, the body is a debt collector ruthless enough to force its demented owner to drink petrol/radiator water/sea water in an effort to exact repayment.

A raging need in hot climates, thirst is more insidious in cold: you may not feel the pangs until too late. But 2 litres (4 pints) of water a day are essential to keep you going efficiently in cool weather, and at least 4 litres (1 gallon) in hot. It is as ultimate as this.

The castaway can fight thirst by sucking a green leaf (which doesn't help physiologically) and controlling his perspiration rate (which does). But in the short run he must find water. And having found it, try to make it fit to drink.

Staving off thirst

Suck something
Try it and see. You may feel risk of swallowing hard object is too great. Choose something smooth and non-absorbent and small: nut/pebble/leaf/gum. Prune is excellent. So is piece of raw onion.

Sucking snow or ice is not recommended (makes you more thirsty, and chills stomach.) If you do, hold melt-water in mouth to take off chill before swallowing. Take a little food at same time to attune stomach.

Cigarettes can help – but also dry mouth more than ever.

Pace yourself
Main aim must be to sweat as little as possible. Water lost through perspiration must be replaced. In a hot climate move as if in slow motion. Your need for water rises astronomically if you are very active in the heat. Conserve precious body water with calculated action when moving about.

Don't rush/panic/run

Cold weather will demand hard work (making shelter/collecting firewood/gathering ice or snow for water) – even so, try to sweat as little as possible (*see Too Cold page 139*).

Rest often. Sleep whenever possible. Work on rota if jobs to be done so some are resting while minimum number do their stint.

Regulate clothing

A hot climate calls for body-cover to check sweat evaporation. Add clothes instead of subtracting them. Button up collar/sleeves/coat. Cover legs. Make head-dress (*see Too Bright page 113*). Spin out your body moisture to best effect by keeping it *in* or at second best *on* body.

Wear white in sunbright arena – white shirt over black coat say. Uncomfortable, yes, but helps to reflect heat rays that evaporate sweat.

You can only be comfortable in hot weather through losing sweat quickly – i.e. by taking your clothes off. And that, when body water is at a premium, is un-affordable luxury.

Very cold weather can mean that sweat freezes. Cut down sweat rate by loosening tight clothing/taking off clothing layers, then replacing everything when you stop (*see Too Cold page 139*).

Keep cool

Cool off in hot weather with damp pad soaked in sea water/urine/alcohol and rub face, hands, neck.

On raft/lifeboat/dinghy soak clothes with sea water, though don't overdo this under raging sun. Unwise to jump into sea (danger of sharks and you may be too weak to get back easily).

Take shade

In hot sun you need twice as much water as in shade. So use whatever shade available – vehicle/tree/rock/dune. Shadow is the key to conserving sweat, and alleviating thirst pangs which would rage more on the move. If no shelter make one from any fabric or gear you have, using lean-to or tent principles. Sleep.

In any shelter allow slits to let air circulate freely in

73

hot atmosphere. Also sit off the ground rather than sprawl on it – it is several degrees cooler 30 cm (12 in) above hot sand/soil/rock. Insulate from the ground with anything available. (Note: it is cooler *under* the surface too.)

Use the shade of night for main movement – walking and working, and get more miles per litre/pint of water than in daytime where sun frics, frizzles, flails and terrifies. You can almost double mileage at night if you *have* to walk.

Don't eat . . .
(a) Anything if water as meagre as 575 ml (1 pint) a day.
(b) Proteins (eggs/milk/fish/cheese) if you have only up to 5 litres/10 pints a day as these need water for digestion. Eat fruit/sweets/biscuits. Plants.

Don't Drink –

Sea water
Whatever is advised here, the temptation will grow and grow and grow. The castaway anguished with thirst thinks that perhaps he *is* different and will be able to take salt water without harm. That perhaps there is some loophole and he'll be all right. Then vague recollections of people who survived by drinking taboo fluids come pounding in. Then what the hell . . .

And he drinks (perhaps pretending it to be accidental). And at first seems the winner. The saline refreshes, revives, assuages. It seems to last too, until he presently is called on to sip again. And again. And again. And againandagainandagainagainagain.

His thirst, whatever before, will balloon into fiendish proportions. And quite soon, with racing pulse, sickness, obscene tongue, blue skin, glassy eyes, deluded and deaf, he will die in delirium.

Sea water *can* be used: for cooling hot body; chilling eye compress when you are sunblind; swilling off salt-encrusted tarpaulins/containers/decks when rain shower is due and you don't want solid salt in supply, *but never drink it*.

Urine
Don't drink, as salt content too high. You become thirstier. Use to make damp cooling pad in burning heat. Or to warm chilled skin in cold.

Alcohol
Consumption not advised. Could precipitate rash actions in survival situations.

Battery water
It might contain toxic amounts of lead.

Fish fluids
Don't drink – even if you have the chance. Many have been found harmful, though there are exceptions.

Glacier water
Rushing melt water from snow areas in mountains contains pounded/powdered/crushed rock. However alternative clear water supplies usually available on hills.

Anything milky, salty, soapy
The exceptions (like coconut milk) are mentioned elsewhere.

Handling Drinking Water

Existing supply
Drink whenever you are thirsty. Little and often is useful to remember. Don't follow the fallacy of rationing the only litre of water into 50 eggcupfuls expecting 50 days of life. Without water in a 50°F temperature you can last about 10 days. With 2 litres (4 pints) you can do around 11 – if not using energy.

By the same token in a desert temperature of 45°C (120°F) you can last about two days without water. But you can still last only two days with 575 ml (1 pint) of water. It is the same for 1.5 litres (3 pints). And for 2 litres (4 pints). Not until you have 4 litres (a gallon) can you hope to survive longer – and then barely another day in this terrific heat.

Drink whenever thirsty. It is the water inside you

that is important. The only way to save water is to *control your sweating*.

Don't be afraid of over-drinking. You *can* sink nearly 2 litres (4 pints) at a time. In blistering desert conditions the body sweats this out in two hours. Besides, you use extra body water urinating/excreting/vomiting.

Drink *enough*, especially in cool climate where you may feel no need to. You still need water and, as in hot weather, it is harmful to ration body's needs when the water it craves could well be available. You always have to make up the water debt sooner or later.

Don't drink water on the first day (unless injured) if you want to feel you are saving water. And of course water needs to be rationed so that everyone gets a fair share.

Remember when drinking – moisten lips, mouth and throat before swallowing. After sudden rain shower drink slowly and deeply.

Never gulp down water when parched.

Additional supplies
When water supplies are renewed through rain/river/oasis drink more than your fill before starting out again. Saturate your body as if it is a bank and you are filling your account to avoid being in the red for as long as possible.

If travelling take as much water as humanly possible in the desert – even at the expense of other gear possibly (*see Too Slow page 247*). Carry it in covered containers. A protective sheath holds 1 litre (2 pints) of water.

Before starting, drink far more than you think you will need. Then en route drink often and in small doses.

The fact you were waterlogged to start with gives you a head start when you run short later.

Questing for Water

Rain
Watch weather signs. Be ready for the rain. Clean dirty containers. Most materials can be waterproofed by

rubbing with candle/butter/wax. Swill boat covers/
tarpaulins/sails in sea to dissolve off salt crust. Some
salt will still contaminate the rain water, but should
not harm you.

Spread out clothes to catch rain. Remember big tree
leaves/tree trunks holes/rock dimples will do the job
for you. If time dig hole in ground and line with
cloth/canvas/plastic. Or oiled paper or leaves. Anything to stop rapid drainage into earth as thirsty as
you.

Rain water can be diverted from leaning trees and
branches by a long cloth wick (torn from any cloth)
leading into a container. Dam or divert dried up
stream bed into rock basin if possible.

Dew
Can fall in great quantities in deserts and barren
places.

Lay out potential dew traps: shiny surfaces like back
of ground sheet/hubcaps/aeroplane cowlings/tin cans.

Dig dew pit – floor it with canvas or cloth or plastic
and heap in cleaned stones dug from under desert
sand. Dew could collect on these and drip to floor.

Drain dew into containers. Mop dew up too. Remember it might collect on nearby plants and stones.
Get up early to check.

Snow
Don't drink when soaked by sea spray. Don't drink
unless (1) no fresh water available (2) no ice in vicinity.
Snow is uneconomical to heat, takes fuel and time for a
small amount of water produced. And you will need 2
litres (4 pints) per day per person.

(Snow can be melted in hand-held snowballs – at
risk of frostbite.)

Put snow into cooking pot/tin/can bit by bit – not in
one packed lump. Compress each bit firmly in. Best to
have a little water already in can before you start. And
when you finish drinking leave some water for next
brew-up. Pack snow tightly in. Tilt can or pot on fire.

Snow from underneath surface is better and more
compact for good water-yield than softer surface
snow.

Snow chunks can be melted on any dark cloth laid

out on rock in sunshine. Lap up water puddles or pour into cooking pot. Best time for heating snow is when cooking, then you use one fire for everything.

Ice
Good water producer. Don't waste fuel though if water available.

Distinguish *old* sea ice from *new*. And only use old ice as it is less salty. Suck it and see if it tastes salty. Old sea ice looks blue, shatters and has blunt corners. New is angular, spikey and a grey-milky colour.

Iceberg ice is good, but it is a dicey way of getting ice (bergs can capsize when even refrozen in a pack as ice below melts underwater faster than above).

Pools on ice floes are usually okay – in old ice. But could be salt-sprayed near water. Use common sense. And taste.

Surface water
Plants don't mean surface water. Look for other signs too. Birds twittering in desert. Birds circling over something. Use animals' trails. Game trails. Trade routes. Investigate holes (or hole) in ground – could be a well or cistern. Stick by an oasis. They are usually linked by trade routes.

Mud
Mop a cloth/hanky/sponge into mud, then squeeze it out.

Plants
Cactus-type plants are worth trying – no matter how leathery-looking. If no knife smash/cut top off/ squeeze. Try pounding on rock – you might get squelchy mush or liquid (don't drink if milky).

Don't waste energy scratching round desert scrub for water-holding roots just under surface. They do exist (perhaps radiating 15 m/50 ft out from some water 'trees') but don't depend on finding them. Investigate by all means – a few feet from the 'trees'. Don't lose a lot of sweat over it.

Plants in jungle can contain fresh water. Try everything. Green bamboo sometimes holds quenching liquid; if split and yellow it may hold rain water; cut notch above each joint if swilling sounds inside. Bamboo makes a good water container.

Vines excellent. Reach as high as possible up thickest vine and cut. Then lop off bottom and point end. Can be drunk straight or poured into cup (note: mouth contact with vine could lead to skin irritation). But don't drink if a milky fluid leaks out.

Green coconuts can hold 1 litre (2 pints) of excellent milk. To get into a green nut find the two 'eyes' at top and drill into them with anything sharp, or smash with sharp rock just below eyes (to remove husk – exterior matting – from nut without a knife, sharpen top of a strong stake stuck upright in the ground into 'axe' edge. Shove nut down on this so stake edge bites between fibres – and keep twisting).

Climbing the palm trees (*see Too Low page 190*).

Underground

Don't waste energy in a fruitless search for water that might be underground in hot climates unless there is some positive encouragement to go on. If you are a water diviner, far enough. If not, save your sweat and energy. Never dig wildly at random.

The following signs in the earth's crust may give chance of water, especially if stained, damp, moist.

(a) Caves – in limestone country (*see Too Low/Too High pages 192 and 198*). Cracks in rock. Springs. Moist places. Stains.

(b) Cliffs – look at base of limestone faces. In lava country cliffs looking like organ pipe columns might seep with water.

(c) Valleys may contain springs/streams/seepages in all kinds of instances – like valley crossing lava band, or gorge in sandstone leaking water at sides.

(d) Hillsides first give you a high vantage viewpoint. Look down to lushest vegetation. If green dig a ditch at base of lush area – and hope it will fill with water. Vegetation on flat desert doesn't mean much, however.

(e) Dry stream beds offer best chance of water at lowest point of the outside of any bend. Terraces above dry river beds may yield water.

(f) Shale/sediment/clay areas are often productive if

you dig – especially under bluffs. If moist.

(g) Sand dunes at seaside: try at lowest point between dunes on outer edge. If you hit moisture don't dig too deeply; you might reach salt water – stop and let hole fill with fresh water. Dig a number of holes (some just above high water mark).

(h) Dry desert islands often produce water in hole dug in hollow about 100m (100 yards) beyond and above high tide mark. Don't dig too deep. About 30 cm (12 in) enough following signs of seepage.

Water Purifying

Treat all water as if polluted. Crystal-clear water could be contaminated. Tap water polluted. Mountain stream might be running from a high village or over a dead sheep.

Risks of cholera, typhoid, dysentery, enteric fever or schistosomiasis too great – even though some survivors have drunk foulest fluids unpurified and got away with it.

Various methods to purify water – viz. when trapped/exploring/using-as-H-Bomb-refuge an old lead mine, good water sources are pools. But surface of these invariably spoiled with skin of lead = lead poisoning if drunk.

So . . . to purify: place finger in ear, collect wax, dip finger in water for wax to break surface tension of lead layer, and drink from small area of now lead-free water (around when your finger was).

Basic steps in much more general use, however, are:

(a) Strain all water through cloth or folded hanky to suspend grit/gravel/sand/rust/dust,

and

(b) Boil hard for two/three minutes (longer preferably) then let any sediment settle. Containers for boiling can be made from length of bamboo/paper box/inner birch bark pan (*see Too Empty page 275*),

or

(c) Add five drops of iodine to 1 litre/2 pints of water (or 10 drops to cloudy water). Let stand for 30 minutes. Sterilize mouth of container with drop of water and wait a little longer.

(d) Water purifying tablets (Puritabs/Portable Aqua)

for which follow instructions on bottle.

(e) Survival straws are good for any water save brine. The water sucked up filters through iodine and activated carbon.

(f) Pinch of salt can improve taste, or pouring water from can to can to can.

(*See also Potassium Permanganate page 154.*)

Note: water seeping through sand into hole will be freshest on top, brackish underneath. Skim off top layer with large shell (also useful for digging). But brackish water won't kill you when sipped in small doses.

Survival still

Providing desert castaway has 2 m (6 ft) square of plastic sheeting he can try to 'milk' the ground. It does not work everywhere, but in many places could yield 575 m (1 pint) a day or more.

Dig hole in unshaded spot 1 m (3 ft) across, and deep enough to contain water bucket (or other wide-mouthed container) 5 cm (2 in) below the lowest point of plastic sheet stretched over hole and weighted down in centre with fist-sized rock. Taper the hole in towards bucket (as shown).

Anchor plastic with soil and rocks and rim of hole. Place rock in centre to weight sheet down. (If you

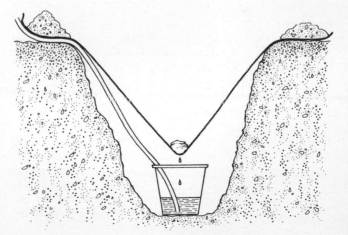

Fig 21   Survival still

roughen undersurface of plastic with sand it helps water droplets to drain more efficiently, but see it's clean.) Note: plastic or rubber tube from container to surface lets you sip water without taking up the sheet.

Sun raises heat of air and soil under plastic to furnace pitch. Forces vapourization of water present in ground soil. When air under plastic becomes saturate droplets form on plastic sheet, it being cooler than damp air below it. Drips trickle into container. Works at night as soil temperature is hot and plastic cool.

Ensure plastic does not touch the earth anywhere and so lose moisture to the sand. Nor touch the bucket. Vapour mist underneath sheet will show when condensation is forming.

Patience is essential. You may get 575 ml (1 pint) in 24 hours, possibly 2 litres (a quart). Water is distilled and may taste flat. Add salt or pour from one can to another. Plastic catches rain too of course. And frogs, snakes and small animals may crawl in and be unable to escape – food.

Note: some sites yield more than others. One above bed of rock could soon run out of moisture. But 575 ml (1 pint) a day is possible even in a bad site. Good site might give 2 litres (a quart) a day for a month. As output decreases be ready to move still to new site. One still is not enough for survival in burning heat, but two or three would help to save you.

Solar stills
Secure these inflatable balls (which evaporate salt water to produce fresh water) to life rafts and float out on sea whenever sun is shining so that you get as much drinking water as can be manufactured.

Desalting kits
If carried in your boat, use when you need water. Keep them stored if you have solar stills working in sunlight, or if it rains.

Too
Wet

4 Too Wet

Fisted by flood, shaken by surf, windmilled by weir –
even a strong swimmer can drown. Swept out to
sea/lake centre/mid-estuary, the average swimmer
may never return alive.

Out of his depth, the non-swimmer often dies out of
his mind with fear. Sobbing/gagging/bubbling, he
might take someone else with him (a panicking,
drowning man finds astounding strength).

*There is no substitute for learning to swim and lifesave
under proper tuition.* Even so, everyone can try to do
something in water and – starting with a deep breath –
possibly survive.

Before splash-down (if you have time)

Kick off wellingtons/waders/boots/shoes.
Rip off tight/heavy/woollen clothing.
Leave on shirt/trousers/blouse/dress/pyjamas.
Stuff clothing and pockets with any buoyant objects.
Buoyancy = balls, inflated protective sheaths, plastic
bottles, bags, boxes, etc.
Remember   buckets/bins/wellingtons-upside-down
float.
Take any raft – plank/car seat/bench (spare car wheels
and tyres may not float).
Don't miss any handy lifebelt or lifejacket.
Aim for anything floating on water.

(Taken-off clothing – e.g. raincoat – should be taken
with you if a swimmer so you can improvise buoyancy
with clothes – see later.)

If You Cannot Swim

1. Gasp in air before splash-down.
2. Grit teeth tight when sinking.
3. Fight off panic.
4. Make like a bottle not a battle.

5. Don't thrash/splash/struggle.
6. Let natural buoyancy bring you up.

Blow-out and breathe-in when mouth breaks surface. Don't try to swim. Nor raise arms. You can attempt to float like a corked bottle in any of three ways – *so long as you don't panic.*

(a) Face up: head back and out of water, body vertical. Hold breath as long as able. Press palms down just below surface when going for air, to make sure mouth is out of water. Breathe out-and-in in close succession – vigorously.

(b) Face-down: back-of-head out of water, body tilted diagonally. Bring face up to breathe with kick of legs and hands press-down. Breathe out-and-in in close succession. Duck face under and repeat.

(c) Knees-up: spine showing above water, head underwater near knees. Hold knees to chest with both hands. Lift head to breathe-out-and-in quickly.

You must not panic. This is the crux. And it is very likely the non-swimmer WILL panic unless he has some floating object to hang on to.

If You Can Swim

Deal with hazards immediately:

Current carrying you out to sea
Don't panic and flounder.

Try to attract attention – waving ripped-off trunks/costume/clothing – and shouting (*see Too Lonely page 15*). Float, tread water or swim slowly.

Check if you are still in depth over long sloping beach by treading water – then sinking. Worth trying in various places even from an apparently long way out.

Work out which way current is taking you. If on the slant then swim with and across it to emerge further along the shore. Swim your favourite stroke, resting frequently when tired. Never battle current direct.

If on an airbed . . . stay aboard in most non-capsizable position. If narrow enough try swimming with hands as you lie along centre. Don't fight against current, but tack diagonally after calculating how far out and how fast you are being taken. And aim to beach airbed further along coastline.

Never be lured into chasing beach balls/toy yachts/air mattresses floating out to sea: better to lose a ball or toy than a life. But if snared into this situation – use whatever buoyancy support object offers for return swim to help save energy.

Getting cramp
Don't panic. Float on back using minimum effort.
(a) In foot: grasp toes and try to bend towards shin.
(b) In calf: straighten leg; try to bend toes towards knee and force back foot towards shin – pressing heel away.
(c) In thigh: bend knee and stretch thigh forward.

When cramp eases, knead with fingers until hardness gone.

Important: stretching combats cramp. And cramp twinges give advance warning of seizure-to-come. When warned, stretch muscles immediately.

In water floating with ice
Swim violently for anything that will lift you out: ladder/boat/solid ice. Bitterly cold water will knock breath out of you, subtract any grip you have in the fingers, and 'curl' you up with shock.

Life span is usually shorter than 30 minutes in icy water. And can be a good deal less.

If water is cold but not cold enough to 'curl' you up with chill-spasm conserve energy (unless a landing nearby) by not removing clothing/swimming far/struggling. Cling on to wreckage if possible.

Burning oil/oncoming boat/gunfire
Tread water. You will have to deflate a lifejacket first. Kick hard and bob out of water. Point toes. Press legs together. Straighten body. Sink below. When underwater sweep hands (palm outwards) from thighs to above head in outstretched motion. Double-up and swim forward when deep enough.

Swim underwater slowly. Use breaststroke/dog paddle/breaststroke-arm-and-crawl-leg action.

Fig 22   Swimming down in a weir

But . . .
(a) Use exaggerated arm action with any of them.
(b) Following kick of feet, glide with arms to side
      before next arm movement.

(Note: swimmers may prefer to dive head first in clear or definitely deep water without risk of injury from underwater obstacles: going sharply down from hips then using breast stroke arm action to thrust deeper and leg kick once feet are underwater.)

In burning oil swim into the wind using breaststroke. Try to splash flames away from head and arms.

Weirs

Swim down for riverbed.

Water rushes over sill into foaming currents which circle round and backlash. Go for the top too soon and you may be bounced like a ping pong ball on a jet of water.

But at riverbed level current is released downstream. Follow this and surface lower down the river.

Whirlpools/falling debris/ship's propellors

Rev away from danger with fast crawl/sidestroke/breaststroke until free from crisis zone. But don't miss any buoyancy at hand (raft/wreckage/barrel) which could help save you – and which is towable.

Swim down, as for Weirs, when in doubt.

Rapids

If with canoe – hang on to it (*see page 96*).

Otherwise swim down any clear tongue of water (V-shaped with point arrowing downstream) among white water. Break into deep water at far end or into slack water behind rocks on way down.

Best way to track down deepest channel is from the top of a rock: then you can look down on rapids round you.

Haystack waves at end of 'V' tongue are usually caused by fast current hitting slow, deep water – barge through with hard determined swimming.

Tree overhanging fast water

Avoid at all costs. Swim/row/paddle hard to evade.

If canoe or rowing boat is snatched broadside in willows, lean downstream so bottom of craft presents its rounded bottom to pile-up of current – and not its cockpit. Pull hand over hand along branches.

Surf

Don't be anxious (especially at start or end of holiday) to get into water without first checking if *safe*. Many casualties where surf has been running. Can be fatal to go in isolated surf. Instead bathe where marker system (red and yellow flags) shows safe beach.

Note: crossed flags = don't go in; when flags planted apart = distance between is safe area (patrolled by beach patrol). There may be other systems depending on beach. Look for notices – ask local opinion.

Surf can be violent. Can turn angry in a matter of moments. It can KO/hammer/exhaust unversed swimmer who thought it shallow and harmless. Children often surf victims.

Never attempt to fight a battering from a heavy surf or being dragged along by a racing current. Survival in big surf needs skill.

Basically only chance for person who does go out in heavy surf (or who gets knocked in off a jetty or sandbank) is:

1. **Try to surf on such incoming waves as possible.**
2. **Grab sand with fists to avoid backwash.**

3. When clear of water scramble above high water mark.

and if swept out in rip current (surf draining back to sea):

1. Don't battle against it.
2. Swim diagonally across it.

After a distance varying from a couple of metres/feet to hundreds, swimmer is clear of rip and should be able to regain shore (though perhaps a kilometre/mile or more down the coast).

Raise arm for distress signal. Keep calm. Float or tread water until help arrives from beachguard/strong swimmer with reel-and-belt/lifesaver (*see page 103*).

If no help near, fight down panic. Swim with breast or side stroke to save energy:

(a) Swim parallel to coast until you get back into the breakers rolling shoreward.
(b) Ride in on back of small surf wave. Just before it curls over and breaks – shallow dive through it.
(c) In big surf, swim shoreward in trough between waves. When big wave approaches get down to bottom and grab sand with fists to avoid being swept off feet by undertow. Push off bottom and swim on once it passes.
Surf livesaving – *see page 103*.

Landing on rocks
Aim for where water hisses up rocks. Avoid where spray shoots up in explosions. Swim slowly in making approach. Save strength for grasping rocks.

Head for destination behind big wave in the breakers. Face shore and 'sit' in water pulling up feet like buffers. If rebuffed on first attempt swim with arms, getting ready for next attempt. Repeat.

Seaweed can make water quieter in its lee. Don't swim over it as much as crawl, grasping the weeds to pull you along by.

Swimming ashore from raft/dinghy/plane wear shoes and at least one layer of clothing. Lifejacket is No. 1 survival aid when facing rocky landing.

Trapped by sheer sea cliffs with no ledges

When trapped and forced to swim for safety through rising tide – aim for rocks in the sea. Keep on layer of clothing and shoes/boots/sandals (for landing).

Make a rope if possible from ripped-up towels/belts/shirts. But it must be long enough to reach from rock to rock. The ideal is a proper rope or line. Handle it as for climbing (*see Too Low page 182*).

Strongest swimmer goes first towing rope tied round his waist (with bowline). Person paying out rope should be anchored to a rock so that if a wave takes the swimmer he won't be torn away too – and can field the swimmer who is being swept away.

When first swimmer reaches a rock, he too anchors himself before taking in the rope for the next swimmer – round the small of his back, feet braced against projection.

Flooded tunnel/cave/passage

When roof meets water – duck.

But only when:

(a) You are certain that waterlogged limit is only brief and caused by lowering of roof into water. And that on other side there will be air space again.

(b) It is essential and only way of escape is to try to wade (or possibly swim) through.

Strongest swimmer goes first – and is prepared to turn back if no way through. Take deep breath. Feel way.

1. **Vent any buoyant clothing which could float you to roof and jam you there.**

2. **Use rope of belts/ties/clothes to keep contact.**

System of signalling with rope:

> One pull: 'I'm O.K.'
> Two pulls: 'Take in rope.'
> Three pulls: 'Pay out.'
> Four pulls: 'I'm there.'

Skin diving

Don't go – without British Sub Aqua Club approved training (which includes survival in emergencies).

Quicksands

Quicksands can never be charted. They can appear overnight and vanish just as suddenly. Retreat fast on any beach when the sand shows any sign of sinking.

Main risk: sand sinking so much under front foot that before you realize it the back foot is following and goes in even deeper as weight of your body is transferred . . . And in trying to check the back foot from going on forward the original foot is driven all the deeper.

Remedy . . .

1. **Try to run – some quicksands are stable enough to support weight of a running man which is transferred** *rapidly* **from one foot to other.**
2. **If running is impossible, try to relax – and lie down on anything handy (coat/beach towel/airbed) which can give support.**
3. **Try not to struggle (or you'll go down more quickly).**
4. **Try to swim clear using breast or back stroke.**

Swimming for Survival

Best energy-conserving strokes: breast/side/back strokes.

Do them in whatever sequence suits. Swim strongly, but never directly against tide/current/wind: progress diagonally across. Sidestroke possibly best for choppy water (easier to breathe).

If swamped by waves, breathe deeply whenever face is clear. Don't shatter yourself with perpetual swimming. Never give up. Keep going. Keep cool and rest often: floating on back/face-down/treading water.

Float on back wherever possible.

Float face-down when water choppy (as earlier). Body will tilt diagonally, back of head is out of water, and by sculling with hands you raise head to breathe out-then-in.

Tread water by letting it do most of work – just hold mouth and nose out. Unless you have other preference, use breast stroke leg kick and scull with hands on or near surface.

A lifejacket helps prolong time afloat (if wearing CO2 inflated Mae West with two cartridges, fire only one at first as inflation from both cramps swimming movement).

It is possible to stay afloat for hours without lifejacket – especially in salt water. And with air trapped in clothing.

Clothing Inflation

Taken-off clothes can be ballooned with air so they support you in water in many different ways. Such make-do floats . . .

(a) Need topping-up.
(b) Need careful handling as if dragged down too hard into water they let out air faster through material.
(c) Need competent swimming ability and ideally, practice, to construct and inflate.

(Note: non-swimmer anticipating ducking and at water's edge could attempt to inflate raincoat/nylon shirt/blouse in readiness, and in absence of anything more solid available as buoyancy.)

Undressing
Get rid of heavy/tight/wide-meshed clothing.

If chance something might serve as float (raincoat say) don't jettison it straight away but keep it floating on surface by trapping air in folds.

Kick off footwear but note – wellingtons held upside down with arms are floats. Hat can be used similarly.

Ideal clothing for floats: shirts/blouses/dresses/nightgowns/pyjamas of man-made fibres or linen or cotton. When soaked they hold air the longest.

Remember not to strip off completely: it is a fallacy everything must come off. Clothing helps combat cold. Only undress from items which offer best air-traps.

Undo zips/buttons/hooks. When disrobing take deep breath after loosening everything and . . .

(a) Take off unbuttoned shirt like a coat (not over the head where danger is it can get wrapped round face).

(b) Rip down shirt front which doesn't button all the way.

(c) Stretch shirt down past waist as alternative.

(d) Rip down shirt front which is buttoned but whose buttons are slippery and hard to undo.

(e) Push down undone pants to knees and further; take deep breath and dip head in as you peel them off using flutter kick to free them.

Inflating

Knot clothes so that in each garment there is only one air opening – i.e. knot both trouser legs of pants near turn-up ends and zip or button up flies or side vents.

Knotting can be done direct in material or tied with tie/belt/stockings/garters.

Inflation is done with fast movement through the air, opening in clothing finishes up under water, clothes balloon into buoyant sausages, and you hold down opening under surface, possibly twisting tight.

Ways of inflating (from clothing floating on water)
. . .

(a) Open garment opening as if to catch butterfly and scoop through air – either from behind back overhead. Or in sidewinder move from side to side. Hold opening with hands below surface.

Then top up by . . .

(b) Blowing up into downward-facing garment opening (*under* the surface).

(c) Taking air below surface in cupped hand and letting bubble fly up into garment opening.

(d) Splashing with a hand into garment opening.

(e) Pressing mouth against wet float and trying to force air through.

Using floats

There are *many* variations by which you can use buoyant clothing. If swimming, blow clothing up during resting period, then carry through water tied round waist when swimming until you need another rest.

Examples:
Skirt Keep on, and float on back. Lift hem, pull towards you then flick through air as if to cover knees.

Fig 23   *Trousers and skirt*
as floats

Fig 24   *Shirt/raincoat as*
float

Curl back hem underwater to hold in island of air.
Dress Slip off. Knot it to block off neck and armholes.
Fill. Grip with hands or possibly between legs.
Trousers Hold inflated like a catapult, chin resting in V
of sausaged legs, first gripping waistband which is
tied with belt down about stomach level.

Or slide arm through V of crutch and bring back
hand to screw-up waistband while swimming one-
armed.

Or put chest through what now becomes U of
crutch, and with each leg as a waterwing swim breaststroke.

Or float on back and grip leg sausages between your
own legs – meanwhile possibly inflating another garment.
Shirt Knot cuffs. Hold collar and shirt tail and balloon
into water to gather air. Quickly gather loose edges
and you have bag and two sausages of air (sleeves).
Raincoat Can be used (as shirt) to make big air sac.

Surviving Wrecks

Everything depends on not panicking. Even in fear-
struck chaos, it is possible to keep your head.

Shipwreck

1. **Put on warm clothing plus lifejacket (cold water can kill in minutes).**
2. **If you have to enter water, swim clear of ship and then stay put.**
3. **Float in lifejacket unless you see rescue vessel or land close enough to reach by swimming.**
4. **In really cold water never try to swim more than a few metres without a lifejacket or some other make-do support.**

Lifeboat practice in passenger liners helps to this end. Note *where* lifejackets are kept in stateroom; *how* lifejackets are slipped over head and their ropes/tapes/cords tied; where *your* lifeboat station is; the *route-markers* to your lifeboat station – say, red arrows; *how many* ship's whistle blasts and gong strokes warn of disaster.

If chaos with people jumping overboard, screaming and panicking – check for floating wreckage before and after jumping. Throw buoyant objects down first into water and land by it/them. Then gather more if possible to makeshift a raft (*see Too Slow page 232*).

Or you may be picked up by ship's lifeboat.

Plane crash

Coming down over water, loosen collar and tie/take off glasses/teeth/sharp or breakable items/high heeled shoes. Get ready for impact (*see Too Fast page 222*).

Put on lifejacket when instructed by crew. Don't inflate in cabin, or you won't be able to move. Hold position of impact until aircraft has stopped – there will be more than one terrific jolt.

(a) Release seat belt.
(b) Do as told by crew.

When outside, inflate lifejacket. Cartridge-inflated lifejacket for child should be inflated before fitting otherwise noise can terrify.

Staff allocate dinghy places for all passengers and crew; take charge of dinghies; transmit radio distress signals; check dinghies all contain emergency rations and first-aid kits (*see Too Slow page 233*).

Canoe capsizal

Stay with canoe. Much more buoyant and visible than you. Collect your paddle if you can.

Don't climb on/roll on to/or try to right canoe. Swim to one end. Tow or push to side and empty.

If danger from weir/rapids/rocks ahead, abandon it in good time and swim to side fast.

Warnings: thundering sound/flying spray/silver line across river (showing sill of weir) . . . all indicating danger well ahead.

If caught in rapids . . .

(a) Hang on to upstream end of canoe and swim down rapids, helping to swing it clear of rocks. Don't bother chasing paddle – someone else may get it for you.

(b) Swim to side *directly* heading at 90° for bank even though being swept downriver at same time.

Fig 25   If your boat capsizes in a rough sea and you can't get a grip on the hull, duck underneath, grasp the seat, and breathe air trapped inside the boat

Small boat capsizal

Stay with it. You are much more visible with boat.

Cling/hang on/climb astride it. But leave it in good time if being swept to some worse fate: rocks/reefs/pier. (*See Too Low pages 187–8.*)

If you can right a dinghy/raft/boat, fair enough. But if not simply keep with it and signal for help.

Flat-bottomed emergency rafts – if capsized – can be righted quickly with calm approach.

Squirm up on to bottom of raft, reach to far side, grasp lifeline (which goes round edge of raft) and skid back into water way you come – so flipping raft over. Often a handle is attached to centre of raft bottom and you can use this. (*See page 188.*)

If a righting line is floating from one side toss it across bottom, move to that far side and, holding it, bring feet up on to flotation tube and pull raft upright until it flips over.

Righting line can be improvised from belt/tie/rope.

Climb in on belly, squirming over thick end of one-man raft.

Have one man in water holding one side down of bigger raft, as rest clamber in over opposite side. But if on your own – climb in over end. Manoeuvre so wind is behind you when climbing in.

Tie yourself to boat if possible by short line before fingers get too stiff to tie knots.

If unable to cling to, or climb on, boat in rough water, swim under upturned shell. Come up inside and breathe air trapped inside boat as you cling on to seat, until weather grows calmer.

Car under water

Cars (and their passengers) crash into water from river banks/road verges/quaysides/quarry tops.

(Note: Always park alongside water or, if no option, with brakes on and reverse gear engaged if facing. Seat belt being used heightens chances of survival in water.)

1. Car will stay afloat longer if windows closed.
2. It is tremendously hard to escape with water pouring through windows. And door won't open be-

cause of outside pressure of water until car is nearly full.

However, if you can act before water is up to window level (which is rare due to impact/fright/surprise) and car is floating wheels down, wind down window and squirm through in nick of time.

Usual course is that car plunges under too quickly for this. Wait, and do as much of the following as your presence of mind allows.

1. **Close all windows.**
2. **Shut any open exterior ventilators.**
3. **Release seat belts.**
4. **Switch on all lights as SOS signal.**
5. **Don't try to open doors.**
6. **Anticipate car tilting – motor end down and climb over into back if resulting air bubble (in front-engined car) forms there.**
7. **Hold door handle.**
8. **When interior water level stops rising (and water pressure inside and out is equalized*) take deep breath . . .**
9. **And open door or window.**
10. **Swim out and up.**

* Let air bubble out from mouth as you rise (air in lungs under pressure will expand as you rise).

Hold up children high in air pocket until time to go. If door sticks, then try other doors/wind down window and squeeze out, pushing with feet. Kick or club through windscreen or window if no other way.

Passengers should try to leave car altogether – if 4 doors. If not possible make human chain – holding hands/clothes/hair so that door can't close and trap someone.

River Crossings

Hundreds of drownings happen each year all over the world when rivers have to be crossed by fording. Or whenever water has to be waded. Always ask: need this river be crossed? Isn't there some way round?

When its *'No'* take survival action. Especially when emergency is forcing your hand.

When to cross
Will volume of river water get bigger or less? Very dangerous if in flood. And if large debris is being carried down. Don't cross. Postpone it.

But if river is normal level and there are imminent signs of rain to come, get across fast. (Note: short steep rivers rise and fall quickly, and flat sluggish rivers take much longer.)

Where to cross
Vital to study carefully. Most important safety factor of all. Time spent is rarely wasted. Look for:
(a) Clear banks. This gives you plenty of room to recover if you run into trouble.
(b) Firm smooth river bed without obstacles.
(c) Crossing free of logs, whirlpools, reefs, eddies, and other hazards in particular downstream of chosen place (which may appear excellent in it-self).
(d) Current should be weak as possible. So choose widest part. Or place where river splits into several streams. Walk upstream (uphill) for best bet.
(e) Depth is important: pick shallowest place. But you may have to swim.

How to cross
Keep some clothes on to combat cold – so long as not baggy. Wear boots for grip and protection against boulders/sharp stones/holes. Carry rucksack (except when you may have to swim). This adds stability and balance through weight, and if packed well it can add buoyancy in a fall. But loosen straps for quick-release if you stumble and sack drags you under.
   Improvise on these basic methods.
(a) Straightforward wading with short shuffling steps. Move at right angles to bank. Face across stream. Hold on to boulders above or just under water (pocket watch). Avoid facing downstream when strong water pressure from behind can fold legs at knees.
(b) Repeat as above but with a strong pole acting as a third leg. Place pole slightly ahead and upstream on river bed then walk past it. And so on. Current keeps pole pressed down.

Fig 26   Supporting shattered person crossing river

(c) If there are inexperienced or weak persons in your team, link arms in line up-and-down river. Weak person goes in middle.

(d) Ideally use a long pole as a rail with linked arms and weakest person in middle. Strongest person is at upstream end. And you enter water to form a line up and down stream, not across the river. If weak person falls/stumbles/passes-out rest of team can support him.

Only use a rope when needed. If as a handrail keep it high so you can grasp it while negotiating boulders. Don't use in wide/flooded/deep river where it can sag under surface.

If someone is trying to cross, he can tie bowline round waist and be paid out (*see Too Low page 183*), but make sure you have room at side of banks – if he falls he will have to be paid out and brought in at right angles not pulled back upstream (and underwater).

Lifesaving

Many lives are lost each year by brave people who try

to save lives but who have no technique. Lifesaving in water means rapid judgment/sound knowledge/ considerable skill/swimming ability.

In many circumstances it is better not to go to help of drowning person if would-be rescuer is not trained, since two lives might be lost.

Non-swimmer can sometimes help by throwing or holding a stick or some buoyant object which someone in water can grab.

It is possible for a strong swimmer, although not trained in lifesaving, to swim out with a stick or some object by which the drowning person can be towed (so long as he is able to hang on to it, and is not brought into direct bodily contact with rescuer).

Fear is greatest enemy of people in difficulty, and endows them with abnormal strength. Strong swimmer (unversed in lifesaving) who decides to go to the rescue must keep away from drowning person's reach and tell victim they must grip the stick/pole/branch he is offering.

Ways by which non-lifesavers might help:

Reach
Casualty may be within reach from water's edge. Fling yourself flat and reach out with hand. Grip his wrist and have him grasp yours. Or if a little further out hold pole/stick/plank/branch – anything for him to catch.

Throw
When further out throw rope or any object that floats.
Beach ball
Car seat
Planks
Spars
Fencing
Branch
Box
Wooden seat
Many things float. Cast around quickly for this buoyancy, and hurl. But don't go too far away – if drowning person thinks rescuer is deserting him, chances are he will panic and drown.

Fig 27   Methods of lifesaving when you cannot swim

Wade
Wading out to drowning person where water is shallow is faster than swimming. Use pole you intend rescuing with to help wading (*see page 101*).

Row
Boat/canoe/punt will be fastest method to someone far from side if craft available. Sight of approaching boat will also help drowning person to hang on longer and stay on top.

Important: on reaching the drowning person don't approach from broadside-on position, or side of craft will be clutched and you could capsize. Go in with bows or stern, instruct him to hang on and then tow to the side.

Swimming-out-to and towing-back for non-experienced lifesavers
Strip off most clothes unless a short distance (and then only abandon heavy or tight clothes). Speed is essential.

Jump in feet first (*see Too High page 205*) – unless you know for certain the water is deep and clear and then you may prefer to dive. Conserve strength when swimming rather than race madly out to victim some way out.

Straight line as seagull flies may not be quickest way

at all. You may have to run downstream of flowing river to try to cut off victim as he comes past. On sand there may be a sand spit which shortens swimming distance. Remember – you must arrive with enough energy.

Take pole or object to offer the drowning person. A strong swimmer will know which strokes suit him best, but sidestroke is strong and reliable for long-ish distances (simple and relatively small energy output). Arms can be changed. You can breathe in choppy water. And face is protected.

Or, if the swimmer prefers, swim on the back – again using non-towing arm to assist in swimming.

But make sure you stay out of reach when you reach the victim and at any attempt to grab you. Keep out of way or break the grip sharply. Only a trained lifesaver should go into rescue at close quarters.

If gripped (*see Too Crowded page 40*).

Mother saving child
Where child falls into water, and there is nothing to reach with or throw, or child is baby/toddler/infant . . .
(a) If mother cannot swim she should get in the water and hold on to side, lying flat out in the water and extending arms and legs to child.
(b) If mother can swim she should go to rescue, then hold child's head, one hand on either side of its face, and swim on the back, supporting child on the forearms and chest, keeping the child's face out of the water.

Surf lifesaving
If *you* are on a beach bordering surf, you may be asked to handle the line and reel (attached to non-buoyant belt worn by lifesaver) used by beachguards. If so, and with help from others if possible . . .

1. **Watch the beltman.**
2. **Pull in when he raises an arm (hand over hand).**
3. **Never pull in too fast and so submerge rescuer and victim.**

There may be no beachguard, but look for the red box holding reel, line and belt. And a hand-wound siren too.

If someone is in trouble and no expert help at hand . . .

1. **Sound the siren to attract attention.**
2. **Read instructions on box and under lid.**
3. **If you feel capable take box to water's edge.**

Feeling capable and being so are very different. If not trained to lifesave, beltman must realize the *many* risks. He must be a strong swimmer/cool/know his limits.

If someone decides to go, re-check instructions. Make sure helpers on the line know the score too. If beltman then you . . .

4. **Put on the belt.**
5. **Swim out, diving under breaking waves.**
6. **Don't grab struggler but stand off and reassure.**
7. **Tell conscious victim to turn back to you.**
8. **Grip from behind holding one of victim's wrists to his chest.**
9. **Raise one hand to be pulled in.**

Or you may find it preferable after turning victim on back to grip firmly above the elbows.

If pulled in too fast from the beach or line snags pull safety pin of lanyard fitted to front of belt upwards. Belt will come undone.

Start artificial respiration immediately if necessary once out of surf.

Hazards

Drowning is the hazard; artificial respiration the answer. Also vital for electric shock/gas fumes/choking/suffocation and other victims whose breathing has stopped.

Get injured to fresh air. And make sure any electrical contact is broken. Then apply . . .

Artificial Respiration

Kiss of life
1. Lay injured on back.
2. Seconds count – quickly clear mouth with a wipe of finger.
3. Tilt head well back and push jaw up to open air route (in 'sword swallowing' position) – vital.
4. Seal nostrils with your cheek or pincer with fingers.
5. Take deep breath, open your mouth wide and seal it tight round victim's.
6. Blow into his lungs. Watch for chest to rise. Then take your mouth away.
7. Watch chest fall while taking next deep breath (and listen for return rush of air).

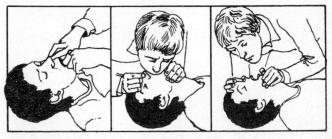

Fig 28   Kiss of life

If this doesn't happen push injured's head further back and try again to get exchange of air needed.

8. Repeat process. Do first 6 inflations quickly. Then at 10 a minute for an adult; 20 lighter breaths a minute for a child.

Note: often possible to clear injured's mouth after first 6 quick breaths quickly. Then carry on at rate specified above.

9. If unable to open or use injured's mouth – use mouth to nose method by sealing injured's mouth and blowing through their nose instead (using same procedure as mouth to mouth).

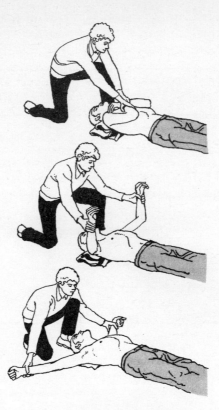

*Fig 29　Silvester method (use when facial injuries make kiss
of life impossible)*

106

If victim is injured about the face use . . .

Silvester method (revised)
Act *Fast*

1. Lay patient on back.
2. Pad under shoulders with coat/sweater/lifejacket.
3. Clear mouth quickly of debris. Check head is hanging back and down.
4. Kneel astride head, gripping wrists.
5. Cross them over lower part of chest.
6. Keep your arms straight and rock down on chest.
7. Swing back and sweep injured's arms up and out to full span (which takes pressure of chest and invites intake of air into patient's lungs).
8. Repeat about 12 times a minute.

Note: it is well worth practising these methods on uninjured people so that you will be prepared in an emergency.

Too
Bright

5   Too Bright

Dazzle is a fireball to the eyeball whether from bomb, zooming headlights, throbbing sun, forked lightning, flaming petrol, glaring snow or electric arc.

Flash comes under/over/sideways – *through*. It is a red curtain. Yellow stars. Pink pain. Orange ball. Thick green light. Black band. Gritty tears. Unless you can help your eyes filter a paroxysm of light you may be blinded (*see Too Dark page 131*).

As subtle as a cosh, glare often advertises its coming – from banner headline proclaiming nuclear war to storm clouds heralding lightning; from repeated car lights dazzle to persistent sunflash from snow. Be ready.

Stopping Glare

Huge flash
This usually signals a kicking explosion either to come almost simultaneously or to follow.

Throw yourself flat on ground. Pull down children/old people/companions with you. If shade immediately available dive and roll into it – under window/in ditch/behind tree. Shout that others stay on ground.

Blink reflex will help you: eyes screw shut/head jerks away/hands mask eyes. Keep eyes shut tight. Prepare for potentially tremendous *bang* by grasping base of skull with interlocked fingers. Wrists squeezing ears. And open the mouth.

Dig elbows into floor. Keep eyes closed. Lock fingers together hard. Force head down. Count 100 slowly before opening eyes behind fingers of one hand made into slits (H-Bomb flash lasts 20 seconds and could fade before blast comes up to 60 seconds later) – keep other hand pressing on neck.

If driving car reflex actions will be to stab brakes/close eyes/fling hand to face. If after flash-shock you have not crashed and are still in one piece keep head down, eyes slitted and make for side as non-skiddingly as possible. Duck below windows and wait for *bang*.

Blindness from gigantic glare may not be permanent: from several seconds to days of darkness is an estimate, but could last longer if flash happens in the dark.

Strong glare

Screen eyes as shown to combat sunlight reflecting from snow/water/sand. Use these protective measures even when sky is overcast as harmful rays can still penetrate and hurt your eyes.

People differ in reaction to strong glare. Even though you may not seem troubled always wear eye protection in arenas of brightness. Penalties for not doing: you will be unable to see far; judgment may falter; night vision could be affected.

Following methods of making eye shades have proved effective – try to use (a) and (b) in conjunction with any one of the others for maximum safety.

(a) Peer from under pulled-down cap peak/hat brim/ helmet rim/eye shade.
(b) Rub bootpolish/mud/grease/burnt cork/anything blackening on upper cheeks and round eyes to cut down sunray reflections.
(c) Make goggles from paper/cardboard/camera film/ leather/wood/plastic by cutting slits in material to peer through. Tie round head with string or laces, tape or bit of elastic from underpants.
(d) Hair, leaves, grass, reeds or moss can be held over eyes by clamping to brow with broad 'tape' tied round head.
(e) A face mask of thin material (say hanky) has saved eyes.
(f) Dark or smoked glasses have disadvantages – they let light in at sides and from below; they can break; they mist (smear with soap) or frost up.

Tie down any eye shade which flaps – like hanky over face – with tape/string/cord. This will stop sunrays reflecting from snow/water/sand – most acute light bounce of all.

Keep using eye protection once your eyes have suffered from sunblindness and recovered. They will

111

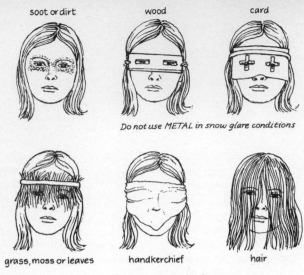

soot or dirt

wood

card

Do not use METAL in snow glare conditions

grass, moss or leaves

handkerchief

hair

Fig 30   *Eye shades*

be sensitive to normal bright light as well as glare, and should be screened even on dull days.

Remember too ultra-violet rays will attack the skin in bright light (before you have chance to become sun-tanned) if you are suddenly pitched into a stadium of glare. Shield body instead of stripping off by:

(a) Buttoning down sleeves and wearing pants over all of legs.

(b) Turning up shirt collar and buttoning up neck.

(c) Making headgear as near to that of Arabs as possible.

Expose body to sun for five minutes a day until you become tanned. Even then only bare skin to sun for short periods each day.

Intermittent dazzle

Possible sources: headlights/mirror/torch. Sudden dazzle from any of these could hypnotize and draw you towards them in moment of glare.

Look beyond and to one side (e.g. driver on British road should look leftwards; jogger on right-hand side, rightwards).

112

Fig 31   Arab headgear

When Warned of Glare

The Bomb

Theories as to what will *actually* happen in the event of nuclear attack change all the time but the survival measures described below and on pages 169 and 256 may influence the odds in your favour.

Warning Radio/TV/newspaper reports of mounting tension; official warning system starting with RED warning (sirens rising and falling to show danger of imminent nuclear attack. Later GREY and BLACK warnings – *see Too Full page 257*).

Flash is first onslaught of exploded nuclear bomb followed by blast then radiation (*see Too Full page 257*). Coupled simultaneously with heat (*see Too Hot page 169* for firefighting) the flash-heat wave throbs from a miniature sun to assault those outside immediate devastation area under this fireball.

Sudden huge flash action already treated.

If warned of fantastic light-heat spasm ahead by rising-falling sirens . . . rush home unless more than five minutes away. Otherwise find shelter. Give anyone shelter if you are already indoors and stay there. If outside seek shelter in any shade offered. Priorities are:

1. Any solid object cover

2. Ditch/trench/gutter
3. Furrow/dip/fold
4. Flat on ground

Cover exposed skin on hands/head/neck with anything available. If nothing, use coat as head-and-hands-hood, and pin down with elbows as you lie. If no flash after several minutes and better cover available dash to that.

If sirens rise and fall as you are driving, pull off road or along kerb – if possible – away from any bottleneck or obstacle that could obstruct fire engine/civil defence transport. Jump out and hurl body into available cover.

Indoors Use anything solid as flash-fire shield; run under strong table/down into cellar/under staircase; crouch below or between windows on flash-side if room bare. Stay until blast past.

If news is bad, advance preparation against nuclear attack: follow advice given at time in newspapers/over radio/on TV. At time of writing, these precautions help if you are given some time (*see Too Full page 257* for advance preparations against blast and fall-out. Also *Too Hot page 169*):

(a) Check under roof for chinks in slates which could let in flash rays – which are also heat rays. Stop them up with non-inflammable material.

(b) Clear away any potential source of fire under roofs/in attics/by ventilators/near windows: piles of papers, magazines, letters, old rubbish.

(c) Whitewash all windows thoroughly, especially at top of house to bounce back flash-heat waves. And to reflect rather than absorb light (later blast will shatter glass but you may have stopped flash blindness/fires/scorching).

(d) Have firefighting aids ready (*see Too Hot page 170*).

(e) Fireproof all burnable material in house (*see Too Hot page 170*). Consider staying elsewhere if house is bungalow/single storey prefabricated house/caravan/or top flat in multi-storey flat. (Best floors in multi-storey offices are middle ones, unless block only four storeys or less high when ground floor probably best.)

Fig 32   Lightning squat

Lightning

Warning Obvious storm signs; hair crackling/ standing on end/sparking; metal on ice axes/spades/ golf clubs/shotguns/scissors singing.

Lightning is one of most unpredictable forces in the universe. It can frizzle you to nothing in a field or club down a house and leave you unharmed. Perhaps 30 km (20 miles) long, a flash of lightning can strike repeatedly in same place (e.g. Empire State Building struck several times each year).

Around 20,000,000 thunderstorms strike the earth each year. Chances of being hit? – about 2,750,000 to one. These points may help you heighten the odds.

Indoors Unplug TV. Put away knives and scissors. Never stand in front of windows. Close all windows (glass is bad conductor of lightning). Sit towards middle of room – virtually 100 per cent safe. Car is one of safest places to be.

Outdoors Keep away from skylines/vertical faces/ underground openings (say caves where ionization of air could attract lightning flash). Don't go blithely into rock face cracks/caves/fissures as lightning could still get through. Any wet surface (cracks in rocks) heightens the risk. Don't get under rock/snow/earth overhangs as lightning can spark from lip of overhang to the ground and fry you in the gap of a ready-made sparking plug.

Trees are generally dangerous – especially lone pines/redwoods/whatever. Solitary trees are potentially lethal. The tip of one tall tree can draw lightning even when surrounded by forest.

Old barns fairly safe to shelter. But out in centre of open field best. Or any flat ground rather than steeply-angled – even small ledge/terrace/etc. Squat on balls of feet if rubber soles, head down. Don't double contact and destroy insulation by steadying yourself with hand on scree/moor/meadow. Poise.

On open/flat/vulnerable terrain lie flat on the ground.

Driving
Warning Whenever you take a walk/car/bike on to roads at night, in daytime fog or snow – remember that dazzle from headlights is dangerous. It takes eyes about four seconds longer to recover from strong glare. At 65 k.p.h. (40 m.p.h.) a car will travel the length of nearly 40 coffins during this time of blind driving. Reduce speed when dazzled. If really blinded, stop.

Don't declare war on the roads. Amount you are dazzled depends partly on amount you dazzle others with your lights.

Don't provoke retaliation from cars/lorries/coaches (possibly with much greater lighting power than your vehicle) by:
(a) Retaliating with full beam against cars you think *not* dipped.
(b) Driving behind cars with headlights 'up', and so perhaps provoking a feud.
(c) Driving with headlights on full beam continually.
(d) By having your headlights misaligned so they dazzle others without your realizing it.

Check handbook for makers instructions on angles of dip and sideways deflection to see if they differ and follow accordingly; align flanges on fluted glass fronts – to spread light – vertically.

If adjustment is needed, car manual gives directions. Or go to garage which has right equipment.

Flash Hazards

Blindness
Atomic flash-caused blindness is usually only temporary – as is sunblindness. (*See Too Dark page 132*.)

Flash burns
High-voltage electricity jumping can blacken skin to alarming degree. Cleaned off, much of skin could well be found intact and nowhere as bad as feared (*see Too Hot page 171*.)

Lightning flash
Can shred off clothing with bizarre effects/scorching/breaking bones/lacerating/stopping breathing – depending where person is and what holding (e.g. rod/gardening fork/camera). Treat accordingly. (Shock, lacerations and fractures – *pages 33, 62–5*; burns – *Too Hot page 171*; stoppage of breath – *Too Wet page 105*.)

Sunburn
Ultra-violet rays redden burn and blister skin before it tans. Can cause pain/fainting/shock. Limit skin exposure to sun in dazzling brightness to five minutes a day. Then cover as described earlier. Also prevent with sunburn ointment. Coconut oil helps.

Treat with shade/rest/coolness. Lots to drink. Fan. Don't smooth on greasy ointments. Don't re-expose until completely healed. No stimulants.

Best treatment – give aspirin and apply ice-water compresses for anything between 7 and 11 hours.

Mirage
Water/snow/sand can shimmer with frequent images: lapping wavelets on hot sand; cities in sky; marching soldiers from shrubs; fleet of sailing ships from birds on water. Don't let mirages rob your judgement or balance.

View from different heights and angles to see them change shape and/or vanish.

Too
Dark

6 Too Dark

What do you do when the light goes out? How do you grope, paw, feel, claw, fumble and stumble out from the darkness? How do you fight paralyzing fear?

Blinded by snowglare/bombflash/acid splash, blinkered by pepper/fumes/smoke, shuttered by shattered bulbs/milky windscreen/powercut, or blacked-out by the night . . . there are few things more overwhelmingly terrifying.

More so when other predicaments crowd around: freezing cold, fast car, strange room, open sea, clamouring forest, burning bingo hall, groaning ice.

When the Light Goes Out

Get safe

Stay where you are if secure. If not crawl/grope/feel to nearest safest point using memory if possible to avoid rubble collapse, live wires, deep water, spilled chemicals, weakened flooring or other hazards not possible to check safely once you are in the dark.

If driving, stop as non-skiddingly as possible. Reflexes should automatically steer you away from any head-on collision – except you may then collide with road edge hazard. Don't cram on brakes when road is open (eye could retain image of what's ahead for about 20th of a second). Brace for crash (*see Too Fast page 215*) if at all possible.

Take stock

Check pockets/handbag/immediate surroundings for sources of light. Memorize. Listen. Smell. Only move if you have to – if forced to shift through fire or flood. If chances of rescue good or of light returning stay and make yourself comfortable. If no immediate chance of aid plan action to help yourself. Try to evaluate best way to signal for help. Think out best escape route: emergency exit/porthole/window or fissure in rock.

Keep together

Don't stray apart. Stay within touching distance of next person. If one person has to go ahead keep contact with them by a rope made from anything handy – belts/ties/towels.

Keep your nerve

(*See also Too Lonely.*)

Don't get rattled – tremendously easy thing to do. Be ready for anything to unnerve you. Phosphorescent objects (like logs in jungle). Spiders' eyes glow in torch light. Dripping water. Bats flying. Wind moan. Shadows. Water gurgle (lapping cave water can sound like voices). Owl/cat/bird cries. Animal screams. Rustle of grass. Cisterns filling. Arctic emptiness.

Noise is psychologically more unnerving than the dark itself. In long periods of darkness combat eeriness by taking/shouting/playing radio/praying.

Moving in the Dark

Use senses in a rough order of priority: (1) sight where possible, (2) touch, (3) memory, (4) sound, (5) smell. Circumstances could change this order: sight might be useless in thick smoke and touch would take over. Sometimes sound can be the initial radar – by throwing sticks/stones/coins to determine dangerous areas ahead.

1 Sight

Light fire (*see Too Cold page 147*). Scrape sparks with boot nails. Use camera flashbulbs and their gun. Employ any battery-powered light (slide viewer/toy spaceship/flashing robot). *Any source of light is* morale-boosting – even a quartz digital wristwatch night light.

Use as little light as necessary, e.g. only moon and starlight if walking on terrain known to be safe. Torchlight spends batteries, bulbs and 'blinds' your night vision. Get eyes used to dark, pupils wide-open scavenging for any stray light rays. Other senses too will get more acute. Ration lighting as morale-charger and energy-booster.

Save light when using it. Don't chain-light precious

matches/lighter/torch by continually striking, flicking or keeping batteries switched-on. Instead conserve at all costs by . . .

(a) Using paper mini-spills to eke out matches. Make from 5 cm (2 in) wide strips of paper which, with a little practice, can be rolled as tight as stiff wire. Start by wetting thumb and forefinger of left hand and rub back and forwards at one corner of paper strip. Suddenly it will roll diagonally and *very* tightly when done properly. Light spill as match flame is about to die.

(b) Burn match/lighter/torch in short spells and use image-retaining powers of eye. (1) Light match, (2) look round, (3) travel several metres/yards immediately light goes out. You improve with practice.

(c) Torch battery lasts longer in short bursts. Keep batteries next to your body when not using, as warmth restores even a spent battery.

(d) Watch with illuminated liquid crystal display (LCD) sometimes gives enough light to read small print (telephone number/address on envelope/ words when jotting message). Can also be used as a marker for any strategic point in dark room – by fireplace/ventilator/window.

Never trust eyesight wholeheartedly in limited light. There is danger of all manner of deception: the 130 m (400 ft) cliff which from above looks like a 3 m (10 ft) step; the deep pit underground which resembles a puddle; the carriage door of train which reflects toilet door.

2. Touch
Use hands as antennae. Arms should sweep as wide an area as possible. Raise hands in front to feel for obstructions. Don't clutch with fingers – and risk involuntarily gripping live electric wires. Instead –

(a) Use back of hand
            or
(b) Clench fist extending one knuckle. Circle fist when probing so any live wire would probably graze knuckle first. And save you.

Go on hands and knees only as last resort. Prefer *feeling round walls* of wherever you are – standing up.

Faster, safer, more energy-saving. Go low to cooler, clearer air in smoke or fumes, however. Or if floor very uneven.

Keep in touch with everyone else. Hold hands, waists or heels (if crawling). Keep hand on wall.

Use pole/billiard cue/branch as feeler to jab ahead in pitch blackness. But extra care is needed if chance of lives wires anywhere around.

Don't rush from place to place in darkened room. Feel round the walls until you find a door or window. Move methodically. Remember your watch can be as a luminous marker for any strategic spot.

3. Memory

Don't trust it, but there are times when it is useful. Moving from landmark to landmark, each approximately remembered, is main memory application. Remember . . . bearings you know like the back of your hand go haywire in darkness/mist/smoke. And it is almost impossible not to overestimate distance in the dark. Counting double paces helps you gauge distance for return trip – count for one leg only.

4. Sound

Noise is deceptive as well as helpful. It is not selective as are the eyes. Approaching car/train/rockfall could be followed almost simultaneously by another (either following or coming in opposite direction) – but noise sounds as all one. The noisier a place the harder to move when using sound as an aid. The ear has no discrimination.

Some sounds are invaluable. Surf/rapids/weirs thunder a warning. Continual bird cries indicate possible roosting place on land. And so on.

Keep quiet yourself when moving in darkness. Don't shout, yell or bawl to fortify spirits (which it *does* do) when moving but make least noise so you can listen for any guiding or warning noise. Or cries of help from anyone else.

Use echoes to help you – they can give general indication of surroundings. For instance . . .

(a) Don't ignore the 'sixth sense' of the blind which many claim is sound-bounce from nearby objects or empty space (note that this cannot be used

123

below the waist – you cannot sense steps/pits/gaps in the ground).

(b) Check any sixth sense you 'feel' by chucking stones/coins/debris in the necessary direction. Forget about trying to estimate depth of any hole by counting seconds until your missile hits, the bottom. You will know if it's more than a few metres/feet deep.

When an escape route is found – say door of smoke-filled room – wait by it if other people not at hand and repeatedly call and whistle so they are guided out to you.

5. Smell
Only a very general guide. Hazards identifiable by odour – scorching/gas/sewerage. Some smells – like burning – carry for miles. Just musty odour of mud flats/mangrove swamps/rotting vegetation or ozone can guide you to some extent.

Aspects of Darkness

Searching rooms
Search dark or smoke-ruined room to a definite plan if anyone could be trapped inside. Make complete circuit round the walls from the door feeling especially in/under/on beds, tables, cupboards where people might have sheltered/flaked-out/be trapped. Finally cross to room centre diagonally from the door to check no one is lying there. But take great care in burning building as centre of floor is weakest point and may collapse.

Handling fireworks/rockets/signal flares
Use available light to read instructions – vital. Don't crouch over when lighting but keep at arms length. Keep face clear. Much better to carry pyrotechnics in box than in pockets – and take out one at a time.

On water
If you don't have to land on a strange coast from raft/dinghy/boat in the dark – don't. Wait until morning.

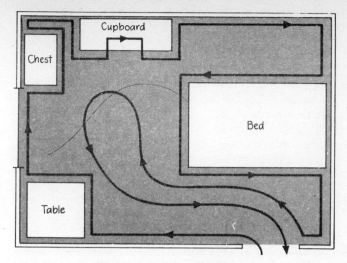

Fig 33   Searching dark room

Out on the sea land can be reflected by clouds: dark-grey shades could mean open sea or land underneath; whiteness might mean ice and snow underneath. Listen for cries of birds coming from one direction – possibly roosting place on sea edge. Listen for far-off sounds of water pounding on rocks/reefs/beach.

On mountains
Wait until morning on unknown or dangerous terrain. Take shelter (*see Too Cold page 140*). Don't try to follow water downhill – very risky: think – *this could entail waterfalls*. Never judge ground by shadows. Avoid having to climb down rock steps in darkness – it is impossible to gauge their real height.

If crossing streams – a real crisis tactic in pitch darkness – *listen*. Noisy ones are usually narrower and shallower. Silent ones are usually broad and deep (still waters run deep).

On snow
Overcast sky means a drastic lack of contrast on snow-plastered ground. It becomes impossible to judge

125

nature of terrain at all. Don't move about in a white-out. You could walk over cliffs, into crevasses, through cornices. It can be hard to stand up straight. No horizon/depth/dimension. Discarded soup cans might look like steel oil drums and vice verse.

If you must move, toss snowballs ahead. Where they land tells you which way terrain slopes. If they vanish you are on the brink of a cliff.

Wait as calmly as possible until settings resume shape and structure (*see Too Cold page 140*).

If you are sure of your position (as you should be) and can confidently navigate to safer ground, a white-out need not be threatening.

In jungle/forest/wood
Any woodland seems extensive at night. Extensive woodland is frightening. Foliage canopy clamps down blackness. Creepers/vines/branches look like snakes. Creaks and groans add to movement of trees. Animal and bird noises are magnified. Light fire if possible (contain it against any forest fire risk). Building a fence round your camp may help to give feeling of security.

In cave/mine/sewer
Keep up morale from the start. Be ready for water-echo: dripping / booming / gurgling. Subterranean sounds can become oppressive. Keep together. Pause on threshold of darkness to let eyes become accustomed to gloom. Don't shout when moving – though it can be a good vent to feelings when resting.

Rest torches and lights frequently. Keep looking back. Many ways to signpost your route – cardboard arrows pointing back, drips of candle wax on floor, length of string, thread or rope. Avoid (in scenic limestone caves) blazing a trail of soot marks, smashing stalactite formations, or scratching on rock – use if possible a method that doesn't desecrate beauty.

Never rush when wading along underground waterways and be prepared to swim if floor suddenly disappears. Shallow pools could turn out to be deep.

Direction in the dark
Stars always give direction.

Northern Hemisphere The North Star is always

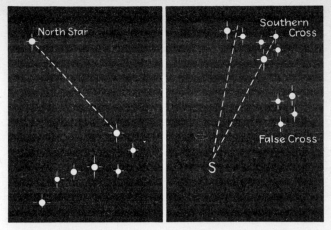

Fig 34   Great Bear and   Fig 35   Southern Cross
         North Star

within one degree of true north. Locate the Great Bear
(or Big Dipper) which appears like a large saucepan
with the two stars on the side furthest from the handle
pointing to the bright Polaris or North Star.

Southern Hemisphere North Star is invisible, but
the Southern Cross indicates south. Find its four
bright stars in a closely-knit cross (don't pick the False
Cross to its right and with dimmer stars set further
apart), and spot the two bright stars set together on its
left. A line bisecting these two at right-angles points
directly south. Also, the line straight down the Southern Cross points south – approximately. Where the
two lines intersect is exact south (in a very starless
sector of sky known as the Coal Sack).

When steering a course by sun (*see Too Slow page 236*)
and clouds obscure it, you can sometimes still find the
sun. Hold knife blade/nail file/plastic credit card vertically on thumb nail (or anything glossy), and slowly
rotate. Unless day is very dark, sun can cast faint
shadow. Midday gives poor results. So does standing
under trees.

Darkness on the Roads

Many more accidents happen at night than in daylight. Road disasters pile up and up in fog/snow/rain.

Hazards double-up when *Too Dark page 120*. When dark *and* wet expect the worst. Gloom plays such a factor in accidents it has been reckoned pedestrians are twice as safe during a full moon.

Danger times: around 1700 hours each week day. And after closing time each night, especially about 2300 hours on Saturday evenings.

Walking

If no pavement walk on right-hand side of road. Wear white – down to a hanky worn round neck or tucked into belt. Shine torch when traffic approaching – from either side.

Crisis point . . . on open road when sandwiched in lights of approaching vehicle and one coming from behind. Scramble up onto verge and keep into side until they pass. Remember – vehicle speed is an illusion at night; you can never be sure.

When crossing in built-up areas: use crossings and islands (or subways or overbridges); don't step on to crossing until vehicles have stopped (see fig of girl jumping on to bonnet in *Too Low page 186*); *listen* and don't dive out.

Driving

Check you have no blind spots. Try this quick test.

Press back against a wall, arms outstretched like wings. Stare straight ahead. Stick your thumbs up. And move both fists forward levelly for 15 cm (6 in). But keep looking ahead. Are you conscious of both thumbs? Especially the right one? If not make allowances when pulling out into (or back into) traffic stream. If blind spot is very accentuated it would be a grand idea to see an optician.

Wide sidepieces on spectacles might cause blind spots. Also – clean your glasses thoroughly in any dark-driving conditions.

Ensure *car* has fewest blind spots : clean windows.

Wipe all lights, reflectors and windows frequently – especially the windscreen (both sides to clear off cigarette smoke and diesel fumes fall-out). Damp cloth best, but screwed-up newspaper makes do.

Back of a comb will clean off ice/frost/snow.

Clean windscreen wipers at same time. Keep windscreen washer water unfrozen by adding meths or a little washing powder (to lower freezing point of water). If wiper motor fails in bad weather, disconnect wipers from motor, tie to a long loop of string, thread in through both side windows, and employ passenger working this endless belt (and wipers) until you reach a garage. Rub screen with cut potato when wipers broken or missing. Or half an onion.

If windscreen is hit by a flying stone and crazes into a milky blindfold, resist temptation to let fly with fist. There is usually just enough visibility to allow a controlled stop.

Push screen out on to newspaper/sack/coat on bonnet with padded hand. Pack up glass after leaving a 'porthole' big enough to see you to a garage.

If a rear light glass is smashed in dark/fog/snow smear lipstick over bulb to keep it red/legal/safe.

When crisis demands tricky reversing and no reversing lamp, use rear flashers to see by on crucial side.

In emergency (puncture/accident/wheel in ditch) reflect light back from headlights to crucial spot with wiped-clean hubcap.

There are three very vulnerable positions when conditions are *Too Dark*:

(a) Instances like big agricultural lorry reversing into a field in dusk or fog with rear lights concealed in the gateway, and whole vehicle presenting a wall of steel across country road.

Remedy Post a look out at worst bend or blind brow nearby to wave down oncoming traffic. In any case . . . switch on full headlights, blow horn and best of all, place luminous-type triangle (sold in garages) on road about 50 m (50 yards) in front of the car.

(b) Any vehicle making a right-hand turn off main road in thick fog.

Remedy Flash headlights as well as indicators, and blow horn when making manoeuvre . . . but listen first with engine off for approaching traffic.

(c) Car driver who loses bearings in thick smog and veers out on to wrong side of road completely lost.

Remedy Switch all lights on. Blow horn. Ease back left with flashers working.

Driving in fog Hunch over steering wheel (you won't be going fast enough to be thrown through it if you have to stop quickly). Always used dipped headlights whether day or night. Sidelights alone are useless on their own. And full beam headlights throw a dazzling white-out ahead.

(Note: proper fog lamps are the real answer fitted under the bumper. But they must be in pairs and used only in fog or falling snow.)

Stick to busy roads. Keep behind a big lorry – but at a distance (so his tail lights are just visible). Truck driver will have best view of road ahead. His vehicle's bulk will stir up fog.

Don't try to overtake him in a clear patch: there is a grave danger that you will run smack into wall of fog while passing – cause of many pile-ups.

Curb yourself. Notice any landmarks on route to give you bearings. Keep wiping, cleaning, washing the windscreen – and keep your glasses cleaned.

Driving at night If coming out of bright-lit building shut eyes as you take the driver's seat and let eyes adjust to darkness.

Most vulnerable times of a long drive are: when trip is taken during period driver would usually be asleep; 60 minutes following a heavy meal; *conversely* some time *after* the last meal (blood sugar level is low); and after fifth or sixth hour at the wheel (even when rests have been taken en route).

Don't exceed 80 k.p.h. (50 m.p.h) with headlights on full beam even on clear, fine night with no oncoming headlights (ideal conditions); nor go over 62 k.p.h (38 m.p.h) with dipped headlights in these perfect settings. These are the maximum safe speeds on ordinary roads (not motorways). Even less than half these speeds could still be unsafe when there is headlight glare from opposite direction, rain and fog-patches. Reduce speed drastically in poor conditions.

Stay awake on long night drive by: changing seat

positioning adjustment; having companion chat (but don't pick up hitchhiker: *see Too Crowded page 47*); playing radio; stopping in layby and sleeping or taking short walk; pulling in at transport cafe or motorway services; opening window, spitting in hand, smearing saliva over eyes – and being stung awake by icy effect of draught on wet eye surrounds.

Don't drive longer than two hours at a stretch.

Signs of falling asleep at car wheel (cause of many motorway deaths) are:

Muscle spasms
Jerking reflexes
Straightening legs
Suddenly talking in louder voice
Yanking at steering wheel
Stabbing at brake pedal
Nodding
Yawning
Blinking
Increased bursts of speed for no reason
Nervous tapping on steering column/wheel/facia

Driver on own *must* be ready for these signs. Passenger with driver displaying these signs should make him stop. But what if in middle of a motorway stretch? Pull in to side and stop for a moment.

How you can wake up enough to get to a safe parking spot . . . Roll head round three times slowly in each direction. Take several deep breaths. Exhale in short bursts through clenched teeth and tight-drawn lips. It works for a short period as does splashing cold water on the face/hair/wrists.

When Eyesight Fails

Sunblindness
Caused by sun flashing off snow/water/sand or just direct. And through your not wearing eye protection (*see Too Bright page 111*). Eyes hurt, water, see red and black, burn, swell, discharge and feel full of grit.

Treat with wet cloth to soothe (but only if temperature is above freezing). Keep changing compresses when warm. Don't use eye drops or ointment. But then eyes become as sensitive as a fast camera film –

131

keep them shaded/screened/protected. Time is cure.

Flash blindness
Flash dazzle is usually fairly short-lived. If not possible to get to hospital, cover eyes with clean dry dressing – any clean cloth and hope for the best. Both eyes usually affected by a huge flash so, if only one eye cannot see, it could be something in the eye from flying fragments.

Something in the eye
Don't rub. Blink instead. Many many times. If on own, try to see with a mirror. If not too painful could be under lower lid. If not visible here pull upper lid down over lower, hold for tears to wash. Blow nose vigorously closing nostril on opposite side. Wet twisted corner of a handkerchief to get the particle.

Helping someone else Stand behind seated patient in good light – positioning head back. Tell them to look up and pull lower lid gently downwards. Then tell to look down and draw upper lid up, rolling it over a matchstick firmly and gently. Never move an object embedded into centre of eye, but only when on eyelid or on 'white' of the eye and when it comes away easily. Clean with clean water.

If object too tricky to remove, cover with clean dressing and get to medical aid as soon as possible.

Blindness after acid/pepper/chemical splash
Act fast . . . sluice eyes with any available water that is clean: tap/firebucket/stream. Dip head under and rinse out eyes – holding them open and blinking at intervals. Flush for several minutes. Protect an unaffected eye with any handy cloth while doing this. Speed is crucial.

Guiding the Blind

Don't despair by any means if someone is blinded (whether temporarily or permanently) and you have to get them to safety too. The following points may help:

1. Never manhandle or propel a blind person unless

vital. Let them take your arm or place a hand on your rucksack/elbow/ankle (if crawling).
2. Always spell out movement directions in every detail. Miss nothing out. Though you may think it hardly worth mentioning – it is.
3. Always address a blind person by name.
4. Success will depend on your tone of reassurance and competence.
5. Don't startle by your sudden presence when blind person thinks he is on his own.
6. Avoid changing layout of camp/room/cave without first telling blind person every detail of the change.

Blinded people have rock climbed/potholed/canoed. They have cycled and ski-ied in tough conditions. Remember this when faced with guiding the sightless in survival settings.

Don't forget the blind dread movement. Especially the newly-blind – the kind you are very likely to be helping. Give every help and don't neglect. Keep shutting your own eyes to 'feel' their predicament.

If *you* become blinded (by temporary flash-blindness say) in known surroundings and you *have* to move . . use a long stick as a probe when on your own. Rather than shuffling head down and crouched, try walking erect, timing each step with the touch-ahead of the stick. Tip explores zone where foot will go before it gets there, right foot steps forward on to it, meanwhile cane switches to where left foot will go. If stick reports sudden step/drop/obstacle your body – with practice – stops upright in balance.

Keep trying this. And place ball of foot first rather than the heel.

Too
Cold

7 Too Cold

Cold that kills is not confined to Siberia. Each British winter sees over half the population exposed to chill-risks normally only associated with arctic explorers/astronauts/Everest climbers.

Blizzards can kill or maim those who have to venture out: postmen, vets, GPO linesmen, farmers, railwaymen, motorists. Freezing cold can cause the death of the baby in pram/man-trapped-in-big-fridge/old-age pensioner in icy bedroom . . . What is the answer?

Awareness of the danger undoubtedly is most of the battle. Even without preparation to beat the cold, knowing its tactics will spur you (at sign of warning shivers and teeth-rattle) into body-warming activity which helps defeat exposure and frostbite.

Keep Moving

Don't wait until you start shivering in coldly hostile country (shivering is normal). Move! and keep moving as much as surroundings allow.

Stamp. Jump. Slap arms across chest. Blow on hands. Stuff hands under clothing (inside pants or under armpits.) Wriggle toes. Arch feet. Bend ankles. Pull faces. Pummel. Cup hands on face. Button-up clothing. Shout. Loosen off tight clothing. Pull ears, nose, lips. Clench fists. Bend and unbend fingers and toes. Exercise shoulders and buttock muscles when cramped. Hold toes up for minute or two when cramped – say on a raft. Huddle together.

Beware of wind and/or rain – they greatly increase chill risk.

A fall into snow-rimmed water can mean exposure. Roll over and over in snow. Jump up and bang off snow. Roll in it again. Repeat until warm all over and snow has mopped out moisture.

Don't spill petrol on bare skin. Don't touch bare metal in freezing cold. Don't shove snow-clad gloves

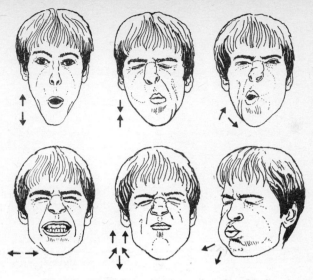

Fig 36   Pull faces (and combat frostbite)

into pockets. Do sit on something else other than snow. Don't chafe or rub sore skin.

Once you are warm keep moving by working. Keep working until warm and sheltered. And then keep *aware*.

Adjust Clothing

Make best of what you have
Wrap in as many layers of clothing as possible.

Newspapers make invaluable dead-air space when insulating round trunk/over body/under you – keep them as dry as possible (under clothing if necessary). If doubtful, remember – newspaper keeps fish and chips warm and windscreens clear in frosty weather.

Paper bags can help when worn on hands when resting. Big paper bag on head (with slits for eyes) keeps in vital body warmth. Anything, like a car jack sack can also hood the head – heat leakage point No. 1. Wear polythene bags over socks in bitter cold-wet.

137

Ring changes of clothing if needed: long college scarf = stomach/kidney/neck warmer-in-one when wound round these parts of body.

Socks = mittens: mittens = socks: short scarf = head protector: balacalva = baby's exposure suit: open front cardigan = can be worn front to back: trouser turn-ups = turn downs (tie round ankles with cord): wool sweater = best vest (wool next to skin).

Best pre-heated gloves if losing grip in intense cold = deepest part inside dead animal. Slit down the front.

Head/fingers/wrists/knees/ankles are all extremities which lose great deal of body heat. Keep covered – e.g. pad the knees (if down on them shovelling, lighting fire, treating casualty).

But don't throttle circulation when you tie. Keep checking that no part of clothing – say waistband – is tight. Hindered circulation means accelerated cold risk.

Waistband accommodating, shove sweaters, waistcoat and cardigan inside – so this clothing is not disarrayed when working and bares stomach. If waistband too tight wear as many layers inside it as comfortable, and leave others outside.

If possible when clothing wet wring out underclothing leaving outer clothing to freeze and protect you in its armour. Don't stand around to do it. Move!

Feet: good circulation vital. Too many socks throttling blood flow in tight boots worse than no socks at all. Keep laces loose-ish. Check feet continually for signs of numbness.

For long periods in wet and cold keep feet as dry as possible, always drying socks each night. If shoes falling to bits or feet continually wet and cold (and no dry change of socks for camp) improvise footwear.

Any strong canvas/parachute/sacking can be wrapped in layers round feet. Insulate layers with dry grass, kapok from vehicle cushions or anything else that might work. Keep fluffing out insulation when possible (*see Too Slow page 231*).

If water in shoes and it is extremely cold keep them on until you reach shelter. So long as you are moving and so long as it is only water (*not* ice) you should be safe from frostbite.

An extreme step to make shoes watertight is – dip each foot in icy water until thin film of ice formed on outside (wriggling toes and arching foot as you do it). No more water can now penetrate shoe until ice has melted.

Control sweating
It is vital not to sweat (destroys clothes-insulation/condenses on skin/can freeze). Don't put on all clothing when working – unless frantically digging-in in a blizzard.

Loosen belt, laces, draw cords, cuff, collar. Take off a top layer of clothing – and perhaps another layer. Sometimes just opening collar, taking off headgear and loosening shirt cuffs enough. Keep cool instead of hot.

When you stop, put all these clothes back on – and more if you feel cold. A tremendous nuisance, but essential for efficiency and fighting frostbite and exposure.

Pace yourself. Unless digging against time for shelter, work slowly/surely/efficiently. Take a five-minute break every 30 minutes.

Care
Clothing should not be jettisoned. It may not seem too cold or serious at time but clothing is never in the way (uses – bedding/foot protection/signalling).

Clean clothes are best insulators. Dirty, matted, holed clothing lets out body heat, lets in cold.

Mend torn clothing – no matter how makeshift. Stitch rents, sew on buttons, patch with any improvised thread and needle (*see fishhook principle in Too Empty page 272*).

Dry shoes away from hot fire. Stuff with grass or clothing or twigs. Turn soles upwards.

When possible beat clothes with stick to remove snow/dirt/sweat. Fluff out all clothing. Shake/rub/scrape especially before going into warmer shelter. Possibly leave frozen outer clothing outside in intense cold as it will thaw inside and become wet. And frozen dry clothes better than wet.

Dry wet clothing when possible. Hang it high in shelters where warm air can reach it. If dry outside, lay clothing out in open, let perspiration condense and freeze again, then brush it out with branches, twigs etc. Fire in very cold weather won't have great drying power – don't hold clothes too near and scorch.

Finding Shelter

Find cover as quickly as possible. Take into account your state of health/tools available/surroundings. You must have shelter, whether plastic bag or stone walls.

Get shelter before dark; before you are panic-stricken; before exhaustion sets in. If lost, marooned, or trapped, wrest shelter from your very surroundings. You can get it almost anywhere.

These hints may help.

(a) In blizzard you won't be able to think straight. If no cover of trees/boulders/car, dig into snowdrift like a mole: keep a hole to breathe and gradually enlarge space round you. Wait until blizzard abates.

Given longer:

(b) Check shelter isn't in lee of bottom of cliffs and slopes where drifts may form. Nor below hillside cornices (snow overhangs), avalanche-prone slopes or in rockfall zones down mountainsides.

(c) Don't camp right on valley floor if potential flooding. Also risk of temperature inversion: mist sinking on to cold valley floor while warmer air rises.

(d) If on sea ice go for thickest ice or biggest floe – away from thin ice and pressure ridges joining two floes.

(e) Nearer you are to timber *and* water the better. They seldom go together, so compromise. Pick timber as first choice for site. If no timber reinforce exposed shelter with windbreak built from anything handy – rocks/ice slabs/aircraft parts.

Shelters

See your shelter is made safe in two important ways.

(a) Ventilate it so exhaust fumes/fire smoke/stove vapour cannot asphyxiate you (carbon monoxide poisoning is common in cold weather camps). One ventilation hole is *not* enough. You need one in roof and one at door to provide through-draught.

(b) Insulate cold striking from floor by every means. Car floor mats, car back seat, plastic car seat covers, rucksack, climbing rope, potholing ladders, sacking, clothes, inverted dinghy, lifejacket, pine boughs, moss, pine boughs, branches.

Keep fluffling out this floor insulation. Make as thick as possible. Never sleep directly on damp earth/slush/cold earth.

When no cover for miles
Keep moving. Build some form of windbreak no matter how meagre in lee of dip in ground or slope. Such areas of utter barrenness rare. Make windbreak shelter of stones. Fill chinks with earth. Roof with any available cover – long rocks, slabs, sticks. Insulate yourself from ground by any means possible – even to sitting in or on rucksack. Keep moving parts of body when sitting it out.

Natural holes
(*See also Too Bright: storm cover risks page 115.*)
Ditches/rock overhangs/caves can all be used if sheltered from elements. Reinforce warmth wherever possible with extra windbreak, roof, floor insulation.

Shelter under and in lee of large undercut boulders – excellent. Build a 'howff' using big rock as main wall with additional windbreaks. Add boughs/plastic sheet/gas cape as insulator. Fill chinks with soil/mud/snow.

Snow
Ready-made insulation. Take into account that wet snow in Britain is quite different from very cold dry arctic snow. Roofs of snow holes will thaw and collapse before morning unless temperature below freezing point.

Don't try to build snow houses or igloos – they are too complicated architecturally.

Simplest shelters are best and remember: smaller shelter keeps warmer longer than big one and takes

141

less sweat to make. And you will need something to use as a shovel/spade.

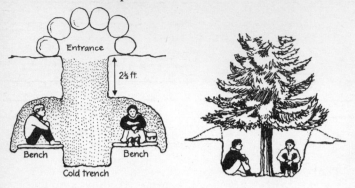

Fig 37   Snow hole and snow-drift shelter

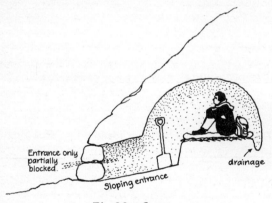

Fig 38   Snow cave

Take off outer clothes when working – so you don't get wet with snow and water.

(a) Drifts formed round large boulders or trees present ready-made scoops and hollows. Crawl into and dig bigger. Make a roof with any other cover you may have – branches/cape/groundsheet, say. It is essential to have something to sit on.

(b) Snow pit. Just dig hole down into snow (can be expanded later into tunnels/chambers/recesses if you wish). Cover with snow blocks, or large snowballs rolled flat-ish to keep in warmth. Make a seat.

(c) Snow trench is very economical in effort. Just dig a slit trench with any tool available in surface snow: flat stone/ice axe/hub cap. Roof with canvas/gas cape/plastic – adding snow on top as lid.

In very cold climate where footprints hardly show (snow is so compact), roof with 'tent' of snow slabs 45 cm × 50 cm × 15 cm (18 in × 20 in × 6 in). Wrest them from rectangular space (as big as you) you first rough out. Dig down to 1.2m (4ft) lifting out slabs. Then lean against each other (offset so you can handle one at a time). If snow isn't 1.2m (4ft) deep – build walls to make the height.

(Note: bottom of roof slabs rest on two 15cm × 15cm (6in × 6in) L-shaped ledges cut along trench edges.)

(d) Snow cave is a bigger job but can be carved within 3 hours for 3–4 people. More if needed. Check walls and roof are at least 60cm (2ft) thick, and it is freezing hard. Channel into snowbank burrowing wide tunnel upwards. Snow can be scraped out or lifted away in blocks. Shape/smooth/slope chamber roof to make non-drip. Chop sleeping bench at height of top of entrance passage and near roof (where air is warmest).

Make cave small enough. Leave a stick sticking through roof for ventilation. Don't completely block the entrance.

Keep everything dry inside the cave. Vital. Restrict trips outside. Mark both top of cave (so people don't walk on it) and entrance (so you don't lose it in blizzard).

Tramp floor of cave flat. Insulate sleeping ledge with anything going – branches/rucksack/newspapers (greased if possible as they get soggy). Smack small piece of snow on to any dripping part of roof to stop it.

Clothing might be dried by your body heat. Don't let boots freeze – wrap up in clothing or plastic bag. And keep them in your sleeping area.

Limit cooking (steam doesn't help). Keep ventilation hole clear. Only use torch for light. And always keep digging tool, whether hub cap or ice axe, ready to dig out in emergencies – like roof falling in.

Ice

Out among sea ice, all you are likely to have are snow/ice/raft/aircraft gear/parachute. Use whatever best on past principles to make shelter and roof it. Snow blocks, ice slabs, wood or metal panels – all help. Be ready to move at once if ice starts to break up.

Trees

Many opportunities for shelters here. Use overhanging branches as roof of snow pit/hole/cave. Remove snow from under tree limbs, or gouge out a bigger hole in drifts round tree trunk, burrowing away from the trunk.

When digging collect firewood: twigs, branches, cones, dry pine needles.

Lean-to shelters are easiest to make – with a fire fanned back towards shelter opening by log or rock reflector. Many variations. Ski sticks-and-ski framework shown is only one. Any sticks/branches/boughs can be jammed and tied into position.

Don't make too elaborate shelter for first night if little time. Better to reinforce on second day. Build facing downwind or cross-wind. Use any fabric from parachute to spare clothing as canopy on the framework. When thatching with foliage, leaves, fir branches start from bottom to give overlapping effect.

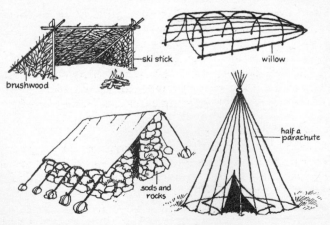

Fig 39   Shelters

144

Tents

Gas cape/plastic bag/oilskin sheet/parachute/sacking. All can be made into tents, whether pup-type, bivouac, wigwam or ridge. Use whichever best for your purposes.

Shapes shown in diagram can be used for whatever you have. The paratepee houses several and a fire burning inside too – which makes distress beacon. Hooped willow tent is shaped like specialist Himalayan climbers' tent. Drape with several thicknesses of parachute material.

Lean-to or ridge-type bivouacs made from a square of cloth, plastic, oilskin, polythene are standbys anywhere. They can be built on flat ground without a means of support except stones. These pull the shelter *taut* (as shown). Tie rocks to bottom edges of sheet with string/cord/laces – which are first secured to sheet by knotting pebbles into fabric (as shown).

Stones/sticks/rucksacks – anything rigid – make the bivouac 'pillars' at each end of shelter. You don't need trees, walls or boulders.

Block ends of shelters with snow, rocks, foliage. Build these shelters in lee of any available (and safe) windbreak. It is worth building a windbreak in very exposed areas.

Buildings

Wilderness country the world over holds many buildings – shacks, huts, cabins, shooting boxes, grouse butts, sheepfolds, encampments, crofts, mine workings, ghost towns in way-out areas.

Up creeks, along canyons, by rivers, behind bluffs, in clearings, along game trails, in basins. All offer extended life to survivor who forces way in (if in obvious use, don't carve up place and leave ruined).

Survival bags

A heavy-duty orange-coloured polythene envelope – folds up small, weighs little and totally encloses you – is invaluable life-saving cocoon if you are marooned out in the open. Keep in rucksack/boat/car just in case . . .

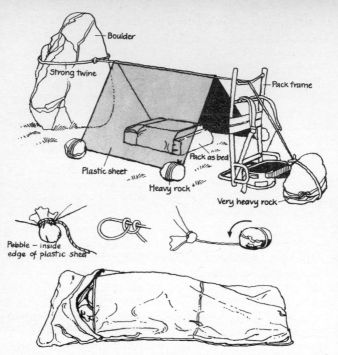

*Fig 40   Ridge-type Bivouac. (Note: big anchor rocks are tied
to sheet with string tying pebbles into edge of sheet.)
Below: Goretex survival bag*

Car

Stay in the car for safety – although not as warm as in a
snow cave (metal conducts heat out radiator-fashion) –
when stuck in blizzard. If stuck for several days it will
pay to make snow holes too, but this not likely in
Britain.

You will soon be rescued if you stay put. Fatalities in
this situation happen when driver panics in snow-
storm and abandons car to walk for help. This could be
several kilometres (miles) away – a very long way in
blizzarding snow. And beaten back – you lose your
car.

If next day is fine, the car almost swallowed in drifts,
then the driver can consider following the road (even if
only visible by telegraph posts) and walking out (*see
Too Slow page 228*). *But stay put in blizzard and at night.*

If no fuel for running engine and heater, keep

146

moving inside the car. Wrap in whatever extra clothing possible.

Run engine when it still works, and there is petrol. But make sure exhaust pipe end is clear. It also pays to cover radiator up. Wait until the heater works. Then switch off engine for as long as possible.

(a) Never run engine if remotest chance of exhaust fumes, either leaked or from tail pipe, being pulled into the car. At slightest signs of drowsiness stop engine and open window.

(b) Warmth and comfort, after period of cold and boredom, are likely to result in sleepiness. Take great care *not* to go to sleep with engine running.

If lock of boot (or any other door lock) is frozen, thaw out lock.

Hold match or lighter flame under lock. Or (easier on your car-finish) warm key with flame and try it then. If still no joy hold lighter under whole key sticking out from lock. Grip with hanky to turn. If no lighter see later for help from car battery.

If you ever leave car to go *short* distance in blizzard or bad visibility – as with any other shelter – signpost it with some form of flag on a long stick so you can find it again.

Plane
Crash-landed plane in arctic cold regions is not a shelter but an ice box. Its metal is a superb conductor of heat in really cold regions so . . . go outside.

If no nearby and superior cover, build snow blocks up under wing or tailplane forming snow house with metal roof. Or make a tent with parachute draped over wing or tailplane and held down with rocks/gear/snow blocks.

In cold, but less cruel, climates (deserts at night), stay in plane. Best to cook outside, though, to avoid carbon monoxide poisoning.

Firestarters

It is tremendous to get a fire going. Hot food. Hot drink. Dry clothes. Warmth. Signalling. Morale booster. The mind boggles.

Be ready for disappointments. You may fail. And

most probably will in poor conditions. Even succeed in very cold weather, and the heat could be so pitiful you have to crouch over it – and scorch clothing.

Patience is essential. So is judgment. Don't try lighting fires in rough weather unless absolutely essential.

Collect available tinder and kindling ingredients which can be warmed next to body.

These tips may help.

(a) Think in terms of building two, three or four small fires and hunching among them (much more warmth) than in one massive fire.

(b) Choose site, especially of first fire, carefully. Not under snow-plastered trees. Not under dripping rock overhang. Not dangerously near car. And so on.

(c) Build fire on rocks/logs/scraped-earth-in-ground – not just on natural earth's surface. Metal parts from plane useful both as fire foundation and reflector shield. Hubcaps are great.

(d) Don't build fire too big = wasteful (unless chance of its being seen or chance to dry clothes). Even then, remember quantity of successive fires better than quality of one.

(e) Make walls round cooking fires to concentrate heat. Or cook in a hole. Pots can rest on side placed rocks/green logs/metal parts.

(f) Reflector of rocks, logs or branches will bend fire outside lean-to shelter in towards you.

(g) Always try to light a fire before dark.

There are many other sensible points: don't build unnecessary fires. And conserve tinder/kindling/fuel and matches. Never waste matches trying to light badly-laid fire, nor use matches trying to light cigarettes when you have lens and sun or sparks from a battery. (When you have a fire, practise fire-friction or other methods in case matches run out before rescue and you have to resort to rubbing pieces of wood together.)

Collect masses of kindling and fuel first. This includes very wet wood which can be dried by any fire you raise.

Tinder
Carry this frailest fuel in tins/bottle/wallet. Bring out in
sun to dry whenever possible. Or any other warmth
source. Aim for dust as dry as snuff – bone dry.

Ingredients: woodworm dust/lint threads/cotton
threads/dry wood powder/shredded bark/unravelled
string/gauze bandage threads/wool fuzz/birds feath-
ers/pocket fluff/bits of bird nests/any dust/dry splinters pounded between two rocks/dry shredded bark/
fat pine.

Add a drop or two of petrol.

Tinder is half a substitute for matches (other half
being spark or heat). Keep adding to your tinder
supply. Take great care of it. And keep your tinder
dry.

Kindling
Collect anywhere. Store. Warm. Keep dry. Consider
anything.

Pound notes. Dollar bills. Family photographs.
Identity cards. Tiny twigs. Resinous shrubs. Bits of
food not wanted for eating. Oily wood/paper/rags.
Wood shaving. Split dry bark. Feathers. Dry glass
hanks. Fuzz stick = twig shaved by knife down sides
to look bit like badminton shuttle, bark curling outwards. Paper spills.

Use roots. Innards of branches, wet on outside.
Drained-off motor oil (drained straight off into ground
before it freezes in arctic cold and you have no container). Birds nests. Dry ferns. Bracken. Palm leaves.

Note: never use all kindling for one fire. Leave some
for next morning.

Birch Bark
Even wet birch bark catches fire. Burns with dense oily
smoke. Peel away fine strips and store large amounts
for firelighting.

Fuel
Collect a terrific supply of anything that burns.

Tree limbs/trunk insides/dwarf trees/scrub. Dung.
Peat. Driftwood. Sea-coal on beaches. Bones. Dead-
wood. Wooden parts of vehicles. Plants (like arctic
cassiope with small white flower, tiny green leaves

and about 30cm/12in high).

Upright dead wood which can be pushed over/knocked down/split up (by driving in sharp stone wedge, or clubbing to bits) is better than lying-on-ground dead wood (wet/soggy/frozen). Green wood will burn on very hot fire. Reduce all fuel to as small-size as convenient.

Try everything for fuel. Use in small quantities. See if it burns. Then use it continually.

Fire Booster
Spill petrol on fuel before lighting it. Sprinkle it on kindling. Use a drop or two on tinder. But never throw it on fire already burning.

Two cupfuls of petrol can start a bonfire immediately from a huge pile of dry twigs/branches/bark if loosely heaped to about 1.5m (5ft) high.

Paraffin and oil are excellent fire primers too.

Fire lighters
Use whatever method of lighting applicable – save matches or cigarette lighter if sun is shining and you have lens. Use paper/glass/faggot-of-twigs to make most of each match or lighter flame. A candle is ideal.

Fig 41   Striking match against wind

Matches
Strike *into* wind (as shown). Tilt match head down into palms to make flame run back up stick if any draught gets through. If matches damp, dry them by rubbing in hair, or holding between palms (head just showing at side) and rub briskly.

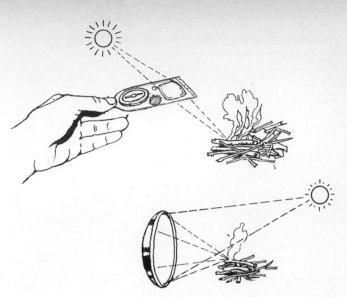

Fig 42   Left: Fire from a large magnifying glass in a Silva or
Suunto compass
Right: Starting a fire from a concave shaving mirror or
headlight reflector

Car/table/pocket lighter
Save for fires. Use sun or fire for lighting cigarettes.

Lens
Try to set tinder smouldering with a convex lens.
Direct lens so sun's rays converge through it in a sharp
point on the tinder. Keep trying new positions until
tinder starts to smoulder. Then glow. Blow gently to
encourage flame.

A lens works equally well either way round.
(a) Two wristwatch glasses sealed together with clay/
    chewing gum/tree sap, enclosed space being filled
    with water, is theoretically sound. One watch
    glass is not.
(b) Any single spectacle lens can be tried. It is not true
    that four spectacle lenses are better than one.
(c) Gunsight lenses work.
(d) The magnifying glass on a Silva or Suunto com-
    pass, used for map reading, could work.
(e) Binocular lenses are excellent. Remove from
    binoculars.

151

(f) Camera with back open is best (wider effective aperture than most optical instrument lenses). Open iris diaphragm to widest aperture. Let sun shine through back where film would be so rays emerge through lens front.

Concave mirrors

Mirrors in car headlamps/plane landing lights/shaving mirrors are good. The larger the better. Sun's rays focus to a point approximately midway between centre of curvature and centre of mirror as shown.

Flint and Steel

Strike sparks from any hard rock (flint, quartz) which doesn't snap or scratch easily – with back of penknife blade/screwdriver/other hard piece of steel. Difficulties: in finding right stone, and then in catching sparks. It takes practice.

Best to try on principle of lighting match in windy weather. Cup hands. Hold 'flint' between left thumb and forefinger, and tinder in palm of that hand. And flick with steel. If sparks catch blow them into flame.

(Note: best tinder here is strip torn from cotton shirt, wound like paper spill so fuzzy edges overlap and spark can be struck into the centre core.)

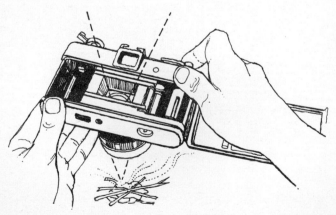

Fig 43   Camera firelighter

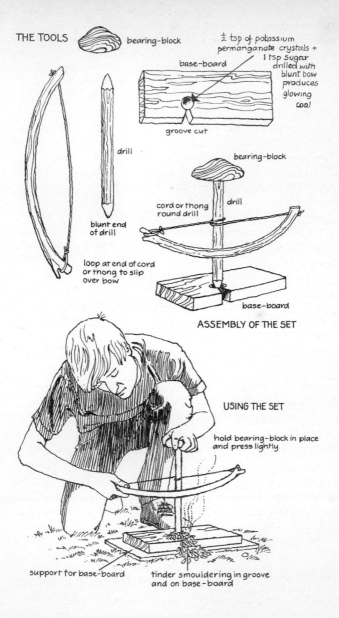

THE TOOLS

bearing-block

½ tsp of potassium permanganate crystals + 1 tsp sugar drilled with blunt bow produces glowing coal

base-board

groove cut

drill

blunt end of drill

loop at end of cord or thong to slip over bow

bearing-block

cord or thong round drill

drill

base-board

ASSEMBLY OF THE SET

USING THE SET

hold bearing-block in place and press lightly

support for base-board

tinder smouldering in groove and on base-board

Fig 44   Fire bow and drill using potassium permanganate and sugar

153

Friction

Very tough technique. Virtually impossible for most people as (1) they don't have practice, (2) they don't have the right wood, (3) conditions far from good. Natives/hunters/explorers using this method carry fire-friction kits with them – like box of matches.

Fire drill is shown. Wood dust is produced and starts to smoulder on top of tinder underneath which, when blown, becomes a glowing mass. Saw bow back and forth to make drill of hard wood spin faster into the soft, seasoned, nonresinous wood base. Note: drill point spins in notch at very edge of wood base so wood dust spills on to tinder below.

Potassium permanganate and fire bow

Mix approximately half a teaspoon of potassium permanganate crystals with one teaspoon of sugar. Pour carefully into fire bow wood base notch. Blunt your drill point a little. Can produce glowing coal which flames among blown-on tinder.

Potassium permanganate and sugar can also be ignited by rotating stick end into it using palms-of-the-hands power.

Potassium permanganate crystals also make an antiseptic (dissolve a few grains in water); stains snow a vivid red (sprinkle on and stir) for distress signal; sterilize water (add a few grains per litre and wait 30 minutes) – pale crimson colour is not harmful.

Car battery

Use battery in preference to other possible car-electrics methods if no cigarette lighter on car dashboard. Take care: burnt hands, flat batteries and sparks in the engine are not good things. Cover up engine with anything from floormats to coat. Make a good job of it – petrol vapour hovers near.

Two methods are possible: either by touching two spanners (or anything similar) across battery terminals to produce sparks. Or (preferable) any wire (like barbed wire off fence) twisted to terminals, then hooped *clear* of car body so sparks can be produced outside.

Don't overdo this method and flatten battery. It can

be effective but don't waste it.

Sparks can be captured on hanky with a *little* petrol dropped on it. Hanky is captured in coil of wire formed in spirals. It should be stiff so it can't droop running flame up your sleeve. Have kindling nearby.

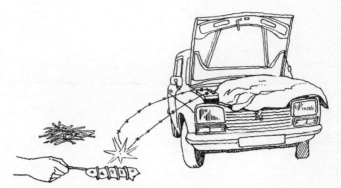

Fig 45   Car battery firelighter and spark-catcher made from petrol-spotted handkerchief held in wire

Motor cycle/scooter/motorboat battery
Same applies.

Firearm
Little powder mixed with tinder may prove effective.

To try for flame, cut cartridge or bullet leaving a very few grains of powder in shell. Insert a little dry cotton (coat lining) with torn and fuzzy edge. Pack loosely. Fire into air. Cloth may float down – burning. Grab and light tinder with it.

Lighting the fire
Vital! Have everything at hand like a surgeon. Never win a flame only to have to run for fuel.

Build kindling into half-pyramid. Leave chinks for draught. Apply your match-fed candle/paper spill/ twig faggot to lower windy side of kindling where you have left an opening (the cut-off part of pyramid) and shield from wind as you do so. Flames should be able to lick from one twig to another.

If lighting by tinder the glowing mass should be

placed in the kindling opening with readily burnable stuff surrounding it loosely – greasy paper, etc.

One way to flare up tinder in calm settings is to drop it (once alight) into ball of dry grass/paper/oily rags tied to a piece of string. Whirl this round the head to try to make a fireball.

Add smallest pieces of fuel to flaming kindling. Add larger pieces only when fire is strong enough not to be crushed. Don't jam wood so tight that draught is cut off. Blow gently. And shield all the time in early stage from being blown out by too strong draught.

Place sticks in large fire in parallel layers. Make each layer-strata at right angles to next layer to give mesh effect for flames slipping through.

Lean sticks radially for smaller fire, feeding them into fire as they burn so that any length does – you don't have to break into short pieces.

Stockpile fuel, especially when wet, next to fire. And keep in overnight by constant re-fuelling, or covering with logs or ashes or leave with soil on top. Take off next morning, add kindling and blow.

Making a Stove

A tin can and heat source is all you need (as shown). Bend, rive, bash, and cut tin roughly into shape of either of these designs. Use tools available (rocks/knife/piton).

Heat source: candle (in this case don't bother to cut tin up but make a few holes); sand/soil/gravel saturated with oil, petrol, or paraffin; plain oil with wick of sphagnum moss/rag/parachute harness (supported with any improvised holder from wire, stone or metal); animal fat poised over lit wick (wick melts fat which drips back on to wick); rubber/wax/electrical insulation which burns best in stoves.

Don't add petrol to stove already going. Initial petrol-stove lighting is risky enough. Let match burn large in fingers then toss it into can turning away and stepping back.

Making pressure stove work
If you lose parts of a Primus or similar stove improvise. Here are some examples.

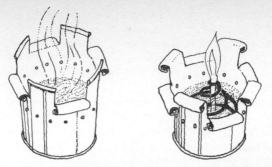

*Fig 46   Left: Stove with oil-soaked sand. Right: Stove with
wire-supported wick.*

(a) Lost flame spreader can be substituted by two
stove prickers bent as cross-pieces over top of
burner top. Or small piece of stone or metal.
(b) Worn and cracked pump washer should be rubbed with butter/grease/oil and re-fitted carefully.
(c) Missing leg for holding tins over flame can be
improvised with build-up of stone, on that side of
cooker. This also shields flame when you light
meths in the first place.
(d) When meths supply runs out, wrap twist of paper
round burner tube in meths cup (in a tight circular
spill). Close stove valve. Pump. Paraffin will foun-
tain out soaking paper. Light this and wait, releas-
ing valve until you re-pump at priming temperature.

Cold Hazards

Exposure/Hypothermia
Cause Sharp drop in body temperature, especially
when wet and exhausted as well as cold. Exposure hits
normally robust climber/sailor/potholer or baby in
pram or old age pensioner living sparsely in cold
house. It is deadly.

   Signs Skin is icy; shivering; paleness; lethargy;
complaints/unexpected behaviour/sudden bursts of

energy (and bad language); stumbling and falling. Slurring speech. Worsening eyesight. Looks drunk.

Treatment *Stop.* And get to nearest shelter (whether behind boulder/wall/hollow). Do not press on travelling. Do not try to stimulate return of warmth by hot water bottles/fire/friction.

Insulate patient so remaining body heat doesn't leak easily away. Get him into a sleeping bag. Or on to thick layer of clothing on the ground. Build windbreak/shelter/tent around. Add warmth with human bodies under/alongside/over (getting inside sleeping bag with the sufferer is very effective).

Use all clothing available (but ensure helpers don't become exposure cases as well). Insulate victim's feet/buttocks/shoulders with extra clothing.

Sugar in condensed milk or warm drink is OK for casualty. Helpers should eat and drink too.

Resistance to cold varies greatly. Old people and young (including teenagers) succumb soonest. Baby in pram has a chance – if mother carries out these principles: i.e. holds infant close to body, covers with coat and blanket, stops loss of further body heat, and doctor is called.

Help Someone should fetch stretcher team immediately. If not possible improvise stretcher (*see Too Slow page 240*). Keep patient well covered during carry to safety. In some circumstances he may have to walk assisted. But usually – don't let him.

Prevention Eat good breakfast; eat chocolate/sugar/raisins through day. Don't plan ambitious route in bad conditions. If someone shows trace of exposure go down mountain/to the shore/out of cave. Don't wait around in leaky inefficient shelter hoping it will pass. *Move* while you can.

Wear anti-exposure clothing. Wear several layers of clothing to provide insulation. Wool is still the best material but is not essential. Windproof pants that don't let heat from knees escape. Windproof jacket which covers wrists (another heat leakage point) and has an effective hood, preferably wired. Wear gloves and balaclava or woollen hat. Scarf and layers of clothing. Anything to trap air (from thermal underwear to pyjamas worn under pants) vital in very cold conditions. And start out in dry clothes. Note: too much clothing = exhaustion in certain conditions (*see Too Slow page 232*).

Frostbite
Causes Often neglect. Not protecting extremities from frost nip. And then not taking action when frostbitten. Touching bare metal. Tight clothing. Uncovered hands/face/ears. Broken limbs very vulnerable to frostbite.

Signs Slight prickling feeling as skin freezes or perhaps no feeling at all; first appears as small patch of waxy numb skin. Feels stiff. If not treated eventually feels like pebbles sunk in flesh. Pain rages. Swelling/reddening/blisters/ulcers. And then numbness . . . with blackened, deadened and dropped-off parts.

Treatment Act at frostnip signs. Watch companions face/faces for waxy spots. Have him/her/them watch yours. Use mirror if on own. Keep pulling faces to avert frostpinch (*see page 137*).

If frostnipped, thaw out immediately with human body warmth. Warm bare hands over face/nose/ears. Push frostbitten fingers down inside trousers to warm on your crotch (or shove under armpits). Frost-attacked feet are best warmed on stomach of trailmate – but keep covered with clothing when warming.

Animal slit down front is good foot or hand warmer. Force limb into deepest part of dead animal.

Never rub/chafe/pummel the part. Nor apply hot water bottles/hot rocks in cloth/hot fire. Nor treat with snow, ice, petrol or oil (all will aggravate condition).

However immersion in warm water may help. Warm drinks too. Keep part covered with dry clothing when thawing out.

Superficial frostnip can be treated so that you can press on to destination. Otherwise (when part is hard and numb) you become a stretcher case. And need a doctor.

When stripping frozen mitts/helmet/shoes thaw out first in lukewarm water – don't pull roughly causing pain and tearing blisters (frostbite devitalizes skin). If pain becomes too severe it might be sign your warmth treatment is too hot and further damage is happening.

Keep patient resting.

Trench foot
Caused by having wet, cold (not frozen) feet for long periods. Can lead to amputation. Feet and toes are pale/stiff/numb in early stages.

Keep feet as dry as possible. Clean and dry socks at every chance. Towel feet gently and quickly after walking wet-footed. Comfort feet with warm bare hands, put on dry socks.

When you have wet feet all time, keep bending ankles/arching foot/wiggling toes. Don't lace up shoes or boots tightly. Sleep with feet dried in warm covering, and raised.

If swelling severe, rest. Protect foot from injury. Lie horizontally and raise foot. Don't rub/chafe/apply warmth. Wait for swelling to go down.

Carbon monoxide poisoning
(*See also Too Wet page 105.*)

Caused through fire or stove burning in unventilated space. Gas is colourless. Keep stove burning with blue flame. Yellow flame = danger. Get outside at once. And keep shelter ventilated in future. Be alert to this danger – especially by not falling asleep in heated shelter.

Getting someone from carbon monoxide-filled space . . .

1. **Breathe in deeply, out, in – and hold breath.**
2. **Get victim.**
3. **If impossible immediately switch off gas source.**
4. **Open doors/windows/ventilators.** (Never follow 4. when place is on fire as draught will create inferno *see Too Hot page 164.*)

Once outside again lay out victim and treat as stretcher case – for hospital. Treat for shock. If breathing stops (or has stopped) – apply artificial respiration.

Insomnia
Caused by cold.

Keep eating through day – especially before lying down. Turn sleeping bag inside out each day. If drying by a fire – don't scorch it. If no fire – take outside when fine, let perspiration on it condense, freeze again and beat it out with stick/twigs/belt. Fluff out the bag for better insulation. Note: sleeping bags with synthetic fillings retain 'loft' and thus warmth when wet much better than down bags.

Don't wear wet clothing in sleeping bag. Sleep in minimum clothing inside. Turn over *with* sleeping bag rather than *in* it. Don't trap head inside if very cold, but it can help to put face in top opening. Keep head covered with a hat or clothing.

Lie huddled together head to toe. Put weakest/old people/children in centre. If everyone in similar shattered state, keep swapping end positions (like penguins). Arrange any dry clothing under, and around hips and shoulders.

Snow blindness
(*See Too Dark page 131.*)

Snow dazzle
(*See Too Bright page 111.*)

Insects
(*See Too Crowded page 59.*)

Hygiene
Clean up regularly all-round. Use lavatory well clear of water or camp – and in lee.

Cut (don't shave) hair and beards fairly short: frost-catchers which have to be thawed. Don't wash when very cold weather, but wipe down if possible with dry or warm damp cloth to uncrust sweat.

Attend to any tender skin. Clean teeth with rag or feathers (soot or salt = toothpaste but don't scour hard).

Combat disease with hygiene, and by conserving energy in very cold weather by getting as much sleep as possible. Keep eating – and drink plenty.

Too
Hot

8 Too Hot

Intense heat can spark off a human urge to leap from impossible heights, fling open doors of burning rooms, hurl water on to flaming oil – and make other errors.

So strong is the fear of fire that the untutored survivor relies completely on his blind instinct of self-preservation. Often the instinct is wrong and means exhaustion/asphyxiation/cremation.

Whether from crackling flames or fierce climate, heat can be kept at bay long enough for escape or rescue – or even while you attack it. But you must keep cool, and deal with first things first.

Before Fire Gets Too Hot

1. **Get everyone outside the burning room . . .**
2. **And then outside the building.**
3. **Shut all windows and doors.**
4. **Call the Fire Service.**
5. **Try to put fire out if possible.**

Approach
Try to estimate where an indoor fire is burning.

If a trail of smoke leads to a closed door, take great care. The fire behind could be small or serious.

Do not fling the door open. Nor open nor smash windows. Any draught quickly fans fire into serious proportions. Open doors also allow flames and smoke to spread.

Where you suspect fire in a room, use the door as a fire shield and inch it open.

Beware if the handle is warm. Crouch when opening so that hot gases and flames will escape overhead. Keep one foot against a door opening towards you.

Always close this door on the fire as quickly as possible.

Getting everyone outside

Shout *'Fire!'*

Sound fire alarm if there is one.

Try to escape at ground-level rather than have to remain or be forced upstairs – escape through a ground-floor window if the doors are cut off.

Shutting doors and windows

Close as many doors and windows as possible throughout a burning building (to help stifle the fire through lack of air).

Never throw stones from the outside through the windows of burning houses/trains/factories.

Calling the Fire Service

Call 999 or shout for someone to telephone immediately if you are trapped.

If miles away from a telephone (in forest, say) run to the nearest house and borrow a bike or car to help you reach one.

Always call the Fire Service, even when the fire seems too small to be worth it. Remember – all fires start small.

Try to put it out if possible

Act immediately

1. **Throw mat/rug/coat over the blaze.**
2. **Switch off electricity and/or gas at the mains.**
3. **Drench with water unless burning oil/fat/liquid.**
4. **Use pan lid or damp cloth or woollen or asbestos blanket to smother burning oil/fat/liquid.**
5. **Never pick up a pan of burning fat and try to take outside.**
6. **Wet surroundings of fire to stop spreading.**

An electrical appliance (TV/washing machine/iron) fire will die down once the current is switched off. If fire still persists after switching off, douse with water.

Portable oil heaters can be cooled off with water. Take the bucket or fire extinguisher to a safe distance, then aim and drench the metal container and surrounding fire. *A spray* is better for this than a jet.

(Remember: when going back and forth to fill a bucket of water close the door each time.)

Fire Fighting Hints

If you live in a lonely rural area, you may be able to extinguish the fire before the Fire Service arrives. These points can help.

Act swiftly. Don't panic. Half-measures are hopeless. Fight fire with a determined concentrated attack at the seat of the flames.

Quench

Water is the standby. Wherever you are, always know where the nearest water is available.

Use buckets/basins/hats – anything in which to carry it. A garden or car-wash hosepipe is best of all. A garden syringe is efficient.

Use any furniture/wet mat/wood panel as a fireshield from behind which you can direct water at close range into the heart of the fire.

Press thumb down on end of the hosepipe or extinguisher to produce a spray, and play this round outskirts of the fire to damp and restrain. Quickly return full jet back at any hotspots.

A non-stop bucket chain of people from tap or stream is effective. But it is dangerous if the fire has caught hold, and cannot be closely approached.

Don't direct water where there may be a risk of hitting live wires which you haven't been able to cut by switch.

Keep jets of water away from burning oil/fat/liquid. However, these can be cooled by a fine spray of water which blankets rather than explodes the conflagration.

Keep water away from burning car engine – impact will dash bits of fire about (and petrol floats on the water).

Smother

Take off your largest coat, throw it on the fire, and stamp or press it down (say on burning car engine). Or use a mat/blanket/heavy curtain.

Act quickly while the fire is still small. A timid attempt will mean the material can catch fire.

Wet the cloth when possible (under tap/in pool/with snow).

166

A damp cloth can snuff out burning oil in a container, stop a small forest fire at birth, and smother flying particles of fat from a blazing frying pan.

Sand, soil and dirt are alternative smothering agents.

Foam and dry powder extinguishers are fine if you have them.

Beat
When a fire is too big to smother, yet not out of possible control, beating it may produce results.

Improvise a beater from anything handy: coat/mat/branch. Really flatten the fire. Use your feet as well to kick and trample.

Restrict
Bundle a burning carpet into the centre of a room with stone floor – so the fire cannot spread. Move furniture and fabrics out of reach of flames.

Never underestimate the speed of a forest/heath/moorland fire. It can move faster than a running man when driven by a strong wind. Rather than attempting to fight this type of fire in its path – run. Try to outflank the fire and move upwind. Beware of sudden wind change. Attack fire with wind behind you.

Overestimate
Always overrate the fire you are fighting.

Check thoroughly once it seems to be extinguished. Pull away charred debris, turn it over and look for red embers. Try to scrape it down with anything sharp – knife/stone/metal-edge/axe.

Charred woodwork is always suspect – even when not glowing red.

Feel and probe hidden corners, ledges, skirting boards, recesses and shelves. Soak finally with water to kill lurking flame.

Warning Staircases and floors are weak after fire. Move carefully round the edges.

When Clothing Catches Fire

1. Roll over and over on the ground.

2. **Try to roll up inside a rug/blanket/coat with head outside.**

If you stay upright you become a human torch with flames running past your face. You also inhale fumes.

Anyone nearby catching fire should be thrown to the ground by the nearest person, and wrapped in any handy blanket/rug/coat. Or helper should lie on top of the burning person.

Anyone burned must be treated for shock immediately, and taken to hospital (*see page 33*).

Moving in Smoke

Thick smoke is a risk to life. You don't know what poisonous gases (like carbon monoxide) it contains.

A wet cloth, held in front of the mouth and nose, helps. It filters carbon particles in the smoke and prevents coughing. Don't be fooled by this false sense of security. It does *not* stop dangerous fumes passing through.

Keep in touch with the edges of rooms and staircases (*see also Too Dark page 122*) when groping in smoke. Go down on hands and knees to avoid dense fumes and keep your mouth low. There is always a 5cm (2in) layer of clearer air above the floor.

If attempting to rescue someone from a burning building try to find a partner to help.

You may have to dash through flames. Wet your clothing to prevent it catching fire. Re-wet if it looks like drying out.

Beware of becoming trapped yourself.

If Trapped by Fire

Don't panic.

Gather the family as far from the fire as possible, and in the best place where you can call for help. Do not jump through windows unless on the ground floor (*see Too High page 204*).

1. **Close all doors between self and fire.**
2. **Seal bottom of your room door with rug or bedclothes.**

3. **Open the window and stand by it.**
4. **Call for help.**

A closed door offers at least 20–30 minutes resistance to flames. Remember – the fire may by-pass it and not attack it immediately.

Someone should stay by window so that people outside realize the urgency of calling the Fire Service immediately.

Anyone weakening from the heat, fumes and fear should be restrained from jumping. He should be told to lie on the floor while you wait by the window.

Consider alternative action if help cannot reach you in time (*see Too High page 203*), and prepare for it by knotting sheets together or throwing down mattresses in preparation for jumping on them.

On no account throw, lower, jump or climb down steep walls from several storeys up until there is absolutely no other alternative. For instance, the flames may force you out of the window, yet there could still be a ledge/balcony/pillar to cling on to.

A little patience and coolness can save life and injury.

You may be several storeys high when help arrives – up 33m (100ft) ladder. Don't panic. Wait for the firemen to guide you to safety down the ladder. Rely on them completely.

When Warned of H-Bomb Attack

Take precautions in advance when warned by Press, TV and radio during a period of mounting tension. Follow the publicized instructions.

Heat-light flash is the first effect from the Bomb's fireball (*see Too Bright page 113*).

Besides whitewashing windows, clearing away burnable materials (say piles of paper in an attic) from places where heat rays can strike (chinks in tiles), the following fire precautions are necessary.

Flame-proof fabrics with:
9 litres (2 gallons) of water
565g (1¼lbs) of borax
450g (1lb) of boric acid

Close all doors. Seal bottom of room door then ...

attract help from open window. Travel to safety on floor in smoke.

Fig 47   Trapped-by-Fire drill

Re-treat any materials with this solution after washing. The material also needs re-proofing at regular intervals, as the treatment deteriorates.

When treating fabrics, dry them naturally hanging up wet.

This treatment would not work with upholstery, but a flame-proofed blanket draped over the piece of furniture would help.

Prepare to fight at once any fire resulting from flash. Gather as many receptacles (from buckets and basins to filling the bath) full of water on all floors – with most on the top floor.

A garden syringe or stirrup pump are ideal for fire fighting immediately fire starts. Mains water supplies are likely to be cut when you need them for aids like hoses.

Chimney fires

Place wire spark guard in front of gate to prevent hot soot overflowing into room. Pour cupful of soapy water over fire to put it out. Detergent clings to coal best. Call fire brigade to check fire hasn't penetrated flue cracks.

Heat Hazards

Burns

First thing: stop flames and cool tissues.

Rip away glowing clothing (peel where cloth intact). Reassure like hell. Vital. Remember – untreated shock kills.

1. **Cool burns with cold water.**
2. **Keep burns dry and clean with anything handy (hanky).**
3. **Don't use ointments/grease/lotions.**
4. **Don't prick blisters.**
5. **Take off circulation restrictors (tie/belt/shoes).**

Dry burnt clothing has been sterilized by fire (if still on patient afterwards) – leave. Remove wet clothing.

Corrosive chemical burns

Swill/drench/sluice with running water when burnt by acids like sulphuric/hydrochloric/nitric.

Take off acid-saturated clothing (but don't burn yourself). Let water drain off burn.

Treat as a wound. (*See Too Crowded page 64.*)

Electric shock burns

First thing: get away from live wire.

Pull mains switch. Yank out plug.

If outdoors the keyword is *dry*

Dry pole/stick/branch to push victim off wire.

or

Dry sack/rope/coat folded extra thick at the points where hands grasp.

and

Dry newspapers/rubber/wood to stand on while rescuing.

Fig 48   Electrocution drill (using a thick pile of newspapers for insulation and brush to push)

As desperate last resort . . . try *vigorous* flying rugby tackle so you are completely off the ground at moment of grab (and current flowing through victim is harmless to an airborne *you*).

If no breathing from patient apply resuscitation (*see Too Wet page 105*).

No heroics, please, if high voltage wires involved. Never climb pylons/poles/towers to help. Or rush to cranes, sand yachts, or other high structures which have fouled overhead power lines. Above tactics (for domestic supply current) *suicidal* when dealing with 400,000 volts.

Telephone 999. Keep onlookers 30m (30yds) back. Only when officially informed that wires are dead by electricity authorities can the shocked-one be approached.

Heat exhaustion
Kills – and a much more likely foe in jungle, say, than attack from crazed gorilla.

Caused by frying under hot temperatures with loss of body fluids and salt. Signs – cramps in muscles; shallow breathing; vomiting; dizziness.

Treatment: give two teaspoonfuls of salt in 575ml (1 pint) of water every 15 minutes in first hour, then every half hour until patient refuses to drink. *Rest and shade extremely essential.*

If short on salt reduce it to minimum – ½ teaspoonful of salt to 575ml (1 pint). Ration it out. Important thing is to increase salt content in body.

Sunstroke/heatstroke

Instant action – fan to cool.

Don't mess about when a sudden collapse (in day or night) is heralded by feebleness/giddiness/dry throat/cold clammy skin/rapid pulse. And it has been *hot*.

You must stop temperature bounding up and up.

1. **Strip victim.**
2. **Wrap in wet sheet/towel/tent.**
3. **Fan, fan, fan with anything handy (shirt).**

Fanning will cool by evaporation if done long enough. Only stop if patient vomits. On recovery wrap in dry sheet.

Too Low

9   Too Low

Anywhere is much too low when your life depends on your clawing a way *upwards* to safety – whether from angry bull, burning office block or rushing tide.

And whether it is a mad scramble up on to speeding car bonnet, back on top of river ice, up into rowing boat, out along tree branches or to tiny ledge above swirling water, the big question is . . .

How do you, possibly paunchy or pregnant, in suit or housecoat (and possibly with crying children), grant your own heartfelt wish: that you would give anything to be higher and safer?

Before Climbing

If time allows:

Take off long coat which could trip knees.
Take off jacket that is tight under armpits.
Pocket watch.
Pocket spectacles (if you can see without them).
Hitch tight pants up over knees.
Hitch skirts up to waist.
Keep trouser side pockets empty.
Kick/scrape/rub mud off shoe soles.
Climb in stockinged feet if wet/greasy/frosty/icy.
Stick adhesive plasters to leather soles.
Wear wool gloves if handgrips are snowcapped.

(Taken-off clothing can be carried up knotted round your waist. Stick not-wanted shoes in jacket pockets.)

Climbing

(Spacecraft mnemonics may help stress key points.)

1. **Imagine footholds are spacecraft launching pad.**
2. **Use feet and legs like rocket motors thrusting you up.**
3. **Don't reach for moon when using handgrips.**

Reaching too high spreadeagles body against face/houseside/wall. Stepping up on feet first, wherever possible, avoids this and is the answer.

Keep looking at feet (but no further down); use knees as little as possible; lower arms when convenient to keep blood circulating; if leg shakes/twitches/trembles take it off foothold for moment or two.

Clean small, dirty footholds with fingers, nail file, comb edge, chunk of stone or handkerchief.

Slap handgrips first with hand. Listen. If they don't sound rotten/cracked/loose – use carefully by pulling down *not* outwards.

Shout *Below!* if you knock anything down. Anyone underneath should cross skull with arms and cower into side.

Using handgrips

Feel *over* edges (as using ladder rungs).

Feel *under* edges (as pulling slot-machine tray).

Feel *round* edges (as pulling back sliding door).

Press *down* with heel of hand.

Feel *inside* any narrow opening with hand *then* clench fist (ape the greedy monkey snatching for nuts through wire netting who cannot withdraw hand when clenching nuts in fist because opening is now too small).

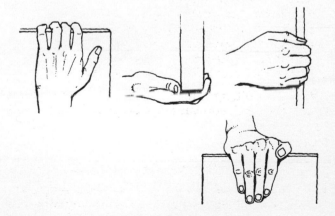

Fig 49   Handgrips

Using footholds

Use anything that supports edge of shoes – rivets/bricks/brackets/barnacles/roughnesses.

Slot toes in vertical slits by twisting ankle sideways first, easing in shoe, then straightening ankle. Release by doing opposite.

Footloop (knotted belt/tie/shoelaces) hung on small projection is sometimes useful.

Back and footing

Place back on one wall and lift feet on to opposite wall of any narrow passage, corridor, alley, fissure or shaft and . . . push.

Press both hands on wall by buttocks to lever body off wall and wriggle higher. Shuffle feet upwards at same time to keep pace with trunk.

(Bring alternate feet to press on wall below and behind you – for more efficient upwards thrust.)

If walls close in (narrowing gap) use knees instead of feet. If walls open out climb whichever looks easiest.

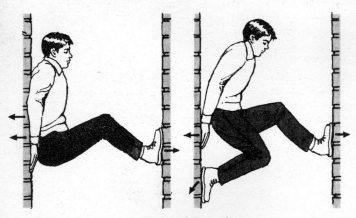

Fig 50   Chimneying

Getting old people and children higher

Old people should only undertake a climb if absolutely essential – and then only to minimum safety height by people pulling from above, shoving from below. At nearest resting point where they are safe they should

Fig 51   *Fire escape – by climbing (being driven up building walls more likely in flood than fire)*

be made comfortable to await rescue while others, possibly, are able to climb still higher.

Use everything to assist: belts for foot and hand loops (helpers will need these too); manhandling by sheer effort. *Old people are likely to let go altogether and slump into helpers' hands – a dead-weight.*

People below Hold/guide/place old person's feet, shoving all the time. Hold their legs too. Support weight on your own head and shoulders. Ensure you have something *solid* to clutch too.

People above Haul/hoist/heave with hands to old person's wrists, then elbows, then under armpits. Make doubly sure you cannot be pulled off by the dead-weight. Strongest pulling grip is wrist-to-wrist.

As height is won helpers below must try to keep climbing so being able to push all the way.

Once aged person is at chest height to a ledge prop their elbows on it and hold them there. Try to grab an ankle next (perhaps lassooing with looped belts) and heave that end up too so the old person can be rolled horizontally on to resting place.

Ensure that if old person lets go and falls he doesn't take you with him.

When ledge is gained, secure the old person (probably too shocked to realize position) with belt or strap to some projecting anchor so they cannot roll off. Treat for shock (*see Too Lonely page 33*).

Children are easier to get higher.

Basket someone small by arms (hands using handgrips), chest, pelvis and thighs (legs thrusting from footholds). Child can use handgrips while adult keeps knee underneath. Or child can be hoisted up ahead while adult below (braced on good footholds) supports youngster by bracing an arm between child's crutch – hand gripping handgrips when possible.

Children can be swung up quickly from above. And boosted up without great effort from below.

If no other way, place child's feet on good ledge, check child has handgrips, then tell child to stay standing there while you climb up alongside to a better position.

Keep calm. Enthuse over progress. Don't sound panicky (even if you feel it).

If child is too weak/young/frightened turn him (or

Fig 52 Child carrying

her) face-in to you and wrap arms round your neck.
Support with hip and thighs of your bent legs while
climbing. But this way is so awkward it can only be
done for very short steps.

Instead, if child small enough . . .

Carry infants and small children papoose-fashion
across back in coat, shawl, blanket, bag, cushion cover
– any handy carrier that can be adapted quickly. Check
child can breathe/is not crushed/cannot fall out. And
check the knots.

Climbing Aids

Ropes

It is 100 to 1 against your finding a proper climbing
rope. Makeshift ones will have to do.

Plastic-covered or ordinary clothes line/church altar
rail ropes/parachute shroud lines/hay bailing rope/gar-
age air line piping/sashcords/wire flex/beach tow-
els/belts/strips torn from blankets/curtains.

All help if they don't have to stand heavy or repeated straining . . . then there is no guarantee.

Test knots by standing on rope or line and tugging
knots. Reef knots good for general use. Reinforce with
half hitches.

181

Ropes are best tied with fisherman's knot (if you can remember it). Very easy to tie. More on knots later.

If line has to rub on rough edge pad with anything soft. Chafing reduces rope strength.

Ladders
Lash short ones together firmly with whatever line available. Two 2.5m (8ft) ladders = 4m (13ft) ladder (capable of reaching many first floor windows or into basements).

Tie overlap of about 1m (3ft). Two people needed to handle ladder most efficiently. Head of ladder may need tying. Always check foot of ladder is firm and anchored/jammed/tied in place. Don't drop.

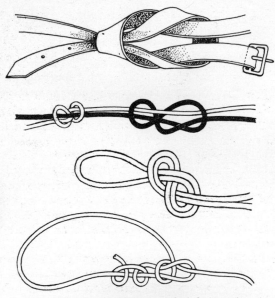

Fig 53   Reef/Fisherman's/Figure of Eight/Bowline (and two half hitches knots)

Using a Rope to Get You Higher

Mountaineering ropework can help in tide-forcing-you-up-sea-cliffs situations – if you have the rope. If you have *climbable* heights. If you forget about the Eiger and stick to basics.

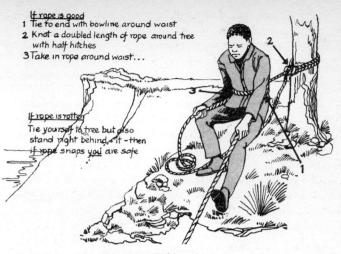

Within the illustration:

If rope is good
1 Tie to end with bowline around waist
2 Knot a doubled length of rope around tree with half hitches
3 Take in rope around waist...

If rope is rotten
Tie yourself to tree but also stand right behind it - then if rope snaps you are safe

Fig 54 Taking in rope

Someone best qualified (strongest/most agile/leader/toughest/clearest-headed) should climb first, towing the make-do rope behind, and tied round his waist by bowline.

At first possible resting place (especially if out of danger) he should search for an anchor (door knob/window/rock spike/tree branch/railings) and loop rope from his waist round it (as shown). If rope is not long enough to make anchor knot *and* reach people below it is possible to make an extra anchor loop with belt, strap or similar.

Down below, next person to follow ties to other end of rope with bowline, either round chest or waist. As he climbs, the top man takes in rope round small of his back as though towelling it.

This back-rubbing method ensures:

(a) Rope or line is kept taut throughout on climber who uses footholds and handgrips like first man up did.

(b) Better chances of line holding if person climbing falls – line handled round human body is given shock absorber as some of strain is absorbed by top man.

(c) No one falls on rope suddenly after drop of several metres/feet clear – which would snap rope.

(d) Someone in difficulty can be p-u-l-l-e-d continuously.

(e) People don't use rope foolishly by trying to climb up it hand over hand.

When second person joins first on ledge, the line can be lowered (still with bowline loop at end) for next person (who like the second did, will wriggle into loop, adjust it round chest or waist, and then climb).

Note: if rope can be lowered at outset by someone from a higher position it should – as here – already be tied into bowline loop at the dangling end. And then rescuer should bring up survivor/s – running rope round waist.

(Old people should be manhandled higher with rope tied round chest. Tie firmly so they can't slip out. Older children should also be roped round chest. Infants best carried papoose-style by adult who is roped round chest or waist.)

It is vital knot stays tied. As bowline is quite tricky and can turn into slipknot, tie rope into any strong knot (over-and-over-and-under-and-through type-of-thing) if you are not sure of bowline. Your own strong knot will look horrible and be hard to undo, but no one will fall out of it.

Such climbing – say on mountain/sea cliff/building – might mean first man climbing more than one short section, each time bringing survivors up to his level.

This means:

(a) First man always aims for a ledge or step big enough to accommodate everyone. *This resting place is determined by length of line – it must reach people below when he gets there.*

(b) If no anchor on a ledge (to tie himself to) first man must try to brace tug-o-war style behind rock/window sill/tree/boulder/fencepost/heels dug in.

(c) As first man climbs he must keep checking that rope he trails doesn't snag round corners, under peoples' feet, on projections – and yank him backwards.

(d) If rope is strong, first man could have reliable person paying it out to him as he climbs (round that person's back with that person tied to an anchor too).

This means a falling first man might be fielded by man handling his rope below – especially if handler's anchorage is not torn away.

But . . . (a) This method needs the rope to be paid out by rope handler so that first man is never dragged backwards when climbing (b) it needs constant readiness for worst by rope handler who is in for a terrific pull if first man does fall.

If this happens, and line doesn't break, dangling man must seize handgrips and footholds and scramble back up to ledge (rope handler taking in line).

(If rope handler below is not tied to an anchor and is in poor/small/sloping/cramped position so that first man falling could drag him down too . . . He should not tie to rope nor pay it out round his back, but merely pay it through fingers to ensure it does not snag and pull first man backwards.)

If first man does fall he doesn't take anyone else with him this way . . . and if he does reach the top then, because of the rope he has been towing, the day is on way to being saved for those below.

Note: When handling rope round back pull sleeves down over hands (to stop hand scorching).

When someone falls, push both hands holding rope in towards pit of stomach to increase friction.

When throwing rope up or across:

Coil clockwise in left hand. Hold coil's bulk in this hand. Take 3 loose coils in right hand. Aim and toss loose coils underarm – letting line run off left hand.

(Never use these last-resort rope methods on spur of moment to climb that nice bit of sea cliff for fun – more rock face rescues happen above beaches than on mountains.)

Aspects of Getting Higher

Leaving ground in a hurry
(a) Vault on to car bonnet about to knock you down.

Pedestrian crossings likely places for this. Can only be done when car braking. Stop legs being crushed/ you being run down/run over by . . .

Leaping for bonnet. Law of chaos prevails (*see Too*

Fast page 214). Do it quickly. Fast reaction is all.

Scissors kick good (uses your bottom to land; one of nature's shields). Head and knees vulnerable points or . . .

Hands on bonnet (as shown) slews you round from front of car – legs splayed.

Fig 55   Pedestrian crossing jump survival

(b) Jump on to footholds when obstacle is solid. Don't reach directly for top of wall rimmed with broken glass/barbed wire/spikes (unless you can grip spikes) – but get fingergrips just below and work feet *high*. Plant one foot flat on top and balance up, fingers pressing down between jagged objects.

If you think fence or wire on wall is electrified test thus:

Are dead animals below?

Are there insulator pots on wire?

Does wire flash in a storm?

Then shave wire with one knuckle protruding from fist. If live wire you will only get a slight shock.

(c) Leap for handgrips when no footholds available. Scamper feet up until you r-e-a-c-h up again.

(d) If no grips or holds for several feet – and if seconds to spare – build ladder from driftwood/stones/coal/mangolds/scrap iron/furniture/hymn books.

Climbing out of water

Take deep breath. Bob up and down in water vigorously, then give strong breast stroke leg kick to shoot you up. Grab handgrip or get elbows over side, and get knee up before heaving on to side.

Docks/pier/quayside with slimy masonry need quick inspection from water. Go for iron staples/wharf timbers/dangling ropes/ladders to help you up.

Steep muddy banks: bob, kick and plunge fingers of one hand high in bank; force *down* with other hand in mud at waist height and kick again; stab toes into side for purchase; keep reaching with one hand, pushing down with other.

Trailing tree branches: grab whatever in reach, kick and work hands along to thickest limbs. If only tips of foliage reachable keep kicking, pull down branch into water and work hands along it from there.

Climbing up into canoe

Don't (*see Too Wet page 96*).

Climbing up into rowing boat

(a) Swim to stern, hang on, bob and kick hard until chest is over edge, then ease into craft, or (b) remove rudder, tie loop in boat's painter and use this as foot loop to climb up. People in boat should move towards bows to counterbalance. (*See page 97.*)

Climbing up into rubber dinghy

Climb in at thick end (most buoyant). Hold sides with

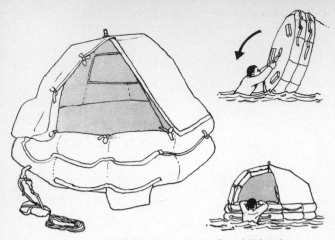

Fig 56   Climbing into an inflated liferaft

hands, kick, heave belly on to dinghy. Crawl and wriggle on.

Lifting exhausted person on bank/jetty/raft
Pull their hands on to bank placing one on top of other while you find best place to stand. Grip their left wrist with your left hand, their right wrist with your right hand. Bounce exhausted person up and down in water (bending your own knees as for any lifting), then heave out quickly, spinning round so they land sitting (and facing water).

If you are not strong enough pull person until at chest level to side. Prop elbows on side. Then swing tired person's legs over on to side.

Use cross-arm-and-spin lift to get light person into a boat. Otherwise pull up until arms over gunwhale. Pad with anything soft under armpits and hoist over (catching a leg as it comes).

Climbing back on to river/lake/canal/pond ice
As soon as you go in . . .

1. **Kick hard.**

2. **Try to bob out before clothes all soggy.**
3. **Spread arms wide on top.**
4. **Slide out.**

Once ice starts breaking further and you are in for good – don't panic.

Chances of survival decrease further out from side you are. Grip edge of ice. Kick hard with feet. Extend arms over ice to spread load. Try to squirm out. Don't give up if ice collapses again. Keep kicking and shoot arms out again. Near side people have ploughed way back to safety.

Rescue action Don't go out on ice near victim. Shout directions. Try reaching with pole/branch/ladder or slide skate or stone tied to line (knotted scarves etc.).

Try crocodile of helpers prone on ice, each hanging on to pair of ankles in front until front person can offer belt (looped) to survivor and squirm back. Beware when ice starts groaning/creaking/cracking/splitting.

Climbing trees
Problem – to grasp first branches not always in reach.
(a) Climb trunk. Possible if riven/whorled/diseased with growths/rough barked/leaning/ivy-grown.

Fig 57   Bicycle/Pole/Rope rescue on ice. Pole is being used to prod the bike on well ahead of rescuer

(b) Build makeshift ladder against trunk.
(c) Take a running jump for branch. If successful swing hand over hand until feet can pad up trunk and hook (by ankles) over your branch. Next – wriggle over on top of branch.

If you need to climb further: pick thickest forks and branches; grip branches at their trunk end; watch feet don't stick fast in sharp forks; check for rotten branches.

Reaching coconuts
(*See also Too Empty page 277.*)

Coconuts grow at top so watch heads. Slim slippery trunks hard to climb. Try lobbing rocks at nuts in range. Or pick small sloping trunked tree and shin up.

For bigger trees use climbing bandage – loop of rope/belt/cloth just slightly bigger than and round trunk. Slide it up trunk to waist height, then step on it with both feet. It won't slip.

1. Stand on loop and reach high for handholds.
2. Hook toes under loop, double knees and pull up on arms.
3. Stand on loop again, and reach once more.
4. Hook toes under loop etc., etc.

And so on upwards to coconuts.

Rope shinning
Many find this impossible. Knack is to reach high with both hands and grip rope between feet too (or feet and ankles), then straighten legs and reach again with hands.

Weak person *might* manage very short rope climb if good rope climber underneath – running fists up underneath weak person's feet, so making footholds. All weak climber has to do is: bend and straighten legs (supported by helper's fists round rope below) and reach higher.

If rope is against wall/rock/tree trunk climb hand over hand and get purchase with feet on obstacle.

Belt/cord/electric flex loops knotted to rope with friction knots can support a person: friction knot won't slip down under tension but can be slid up rope when

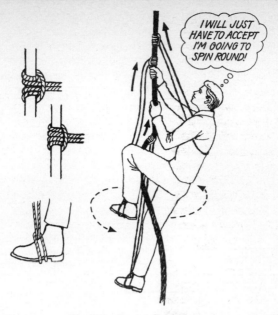

Fig 58 Rope climbing

not loaded. Three loops needed – two for feet, one for round person's body. An exhausting last resort method. (Knots are called Prusik knots.)

Climbing Ladders

Rigid ladders Grip rungs not sides. Have someone at bottom if possible.

Rope ladders Cross hands behind ladder and grip side ropes (rungs might snap). Step on rungs as conventional ladder. Fold arms behind to rest.

Wire ladders Grip rungs behind, palms facing you. If hanging in space alternate legs go behind with heels placed over rungs. But if ladder rests against wall place toes in orthodox ladder style (to toe rungs away from side).

Scaling girders/pylons/scaffolding

Much in common with ladders, but steeper. Rivets/brackets/flanges make useful footholds as well as obvious struts/cross pieces/angles.

Up buildings

(a) Open windows by smashing glass with shoe/ handbag/fist (*see Too Lonely page 21*). Punch straight. Other hand and elbow props you on window sill.

(b) Climb drainpipes hugging with knees, slotting toes in behind. Pull *down* not *out*. Test-shake each pipe section first.

(c) Lightning conductors: test-pull; use toes on building footholds; don't pull outwards.

(d) Roof tiles are best negotiated in socks. 'Sit' on one leg, foot tucked up behind you and press down with hands. Thigh below you spreads and grips like a tyre. But sit up straight.

Make for any handgrips: roof edge/TV aerial cable/holes. Last resort – rip off tiles and you may find support underneath.

(e) Shin up on to ledges/sills/balustrades by pulling on arms, throwing elbows on, scurrying feet up masonry, pressing down with hands, throwing knee or foot on – and straightening up.

(Beware of stonework cracking/crumbling/ powdering/snapping when you put weight on it. Take weight on feet when possible.)

Up mountainside

Pick easiest-looking way to by-pass precipices/snow slopes / ice walls / shale fans / waterfalls / very steep ground (*see also Too Slow page 238*).

When *forced* to climb with hands as well as feet – and there is definitely no other way – follow principles used so far. And these extra points . . .

(a) Climb *rock* faces where obviously easy-angled/ ledgey/possible. Aim for zones with ledges, terraces, platforms and a visible way to top. Gullies/ rifts/chimneys give most enclosed, secure-feeling route but there could be nasty bits hidden in their confines.

Use judgement. If you get gripped come back down (*see Too High page 198*) and try elsewhere. Use rope methods mentioned earlier.

(b) Climb steep *shale* by punching with toes then digging with fingers. Stand straight. Always have three points of contact with the slope while fourth (hand or foot) is digging or punching.

(c) Climb *snow* slopes similarly.

(Avoid avalanche risk – *see also Too Fast page 223* – on any hillside by steering clear of gullies in heavy snow conditions. Innocent-looking slopes over 14° can slip when lying new or thawing on old/hard snow/ice. Test risk by tossing rocks on slope. Snowballs rolling down is bad sign.)

More . . . keep off ground below snow cornices – overhangs – on hillside skylines which can thunder down without warning in thaw conditions.

Climb snow by punching in with toes. Let weight of leg kicking do work. Don't make footsteps too big. Stand straight. Always have three points of contact. Balance with hands (wrapped in anthing warm). When slope feels steep kick steps in zigzags. Kick steps close together. Kick extra big steps at corners of zig zags.

Make stabber in lieu of ice axe out of anything sharp – stone/spike/tool/knife. This helps hack out grips and holds, ledges and pockets. It is essential as a brake if you fall. (*See Too High page 202*.)

(d) Keep off ice slopes. Ice skin on rocks, if only for a few feet, can be chipped off with lump of rock – then climb over in stockinged feet.

But don't drop footgear – have it passed by hand, or carry it tied to you by laces. And remember frostbite risk (*see Too Cold page 159*). Weigh the priorities.

(e) Anchorage usually non-existent on snow/ice. Only use rope if some form of anchor available – boulders/long poles/ice axes. *But* everyone should carry some form of stabber.

Crevasse Rescue

One man can raise companion by simple technique if fallen is roped/conscious/able to help/can be reached with another rope or other end of rope to which he is already tied/if anchors available for rope (ice axes/rocks/poles/ice bollards). Two anchors a must.

(a) Anchor rope from fallen (or both ropes if he is tied in middle of a threesome).

(b) Top man takes up tug-o-war position by 2nd near-by anchor.

(c) Lowers rope with loop tied at end.

(d) Fallen slips foot in this and bends knee.

(e) Top man pulls in foot-loop rope and anchors it.

(f) Then he moves to waist rope and takes in as . . .

(g) Fallen straightens leg in footloop.

And so on, with top man alternately pulling up and anchoring each rope in turn, and fallen bending and straightening leg attached to footloop. With more than one top man process becomes easier – but for fallen it is exhausting task.

Important – lower footloop to fallen as soon as possible to relieve his waist of strangulation strain. If fallen is unconscious or unable to reach footloop go for help (if at all possible).

It is possible to shin up single rope using loops and Prusik knot method (*see page 190*). Definitely a very last resort.

The baboon hang is a way to relieve stress on waist of hanging in space on a rope (after only a few minutes thus you asphyxiate). Check knot is in front of stomach. With a jerk, tip yourself upside down – bending legs over ever further to maintain position.

Prevention Only cross glaciers/crevassed regions when no way round. Keep eyes open for crevasse threats. Probe ahead with poles or throw rocks. Go well round potential crevasse if doubtful. Blue tint sometimes signposts big rift below . . .

Underground

(*See also Too Dark page 126.*)

Clamber to safety on high ledge above water level when sudden flooding risk in cave/pothole/sewer/subway/Métro/London tube/mine/tunnel. Or when marooned underground with injured person or lost – and water level might rise before rescue arrives.

Use climbing principles. Take extra care because of darkness and subterranean slime on stone. Stalactite deposit in caves = ultra slippery. Clean wet stockinged feet better than rubber soles if you *have* to climb.

Big stalagmites (stalactites which grow *up*) make good rope anchors/handgrips/foot pedestals.

Subterranean safety

Keep pace of everyone to that of slowest/weakest/feeblest.
Don't stray apart.
Keep bunched in single file.
Keep looking behind to memorize rear view.
Leave arrows (cardboard/soot/scratched) pointing back.
Leave candle/arrow where you enter big chamber.
Move as though roofs/walls/floor booby-trapped.
Strongest swimmer probes first when way is waterlogged.
Follow through wading.
Only skirt water if easy traverse alongside.

Accident procedure

Especially in caves and potholes. When someone is injured or has collapsed . . .

1. **Make sure everyone in party is safe.**
2. **Get casualty to safest place even if you have to lift or lower – unless spine injury suspected (***see Too Fast page 226***).**
3. **Keep casualty warm and as comfortable as possible and render first-aid. Sacrifice your own clothing.**
4. **Messengers go for help (***see Too Lonely page 25***).**
5. **Remaining companions keep cheerful/build better casualty base/help keep warm/comfort/combat dark.**

Prevention When going to explore caves/potholes/old mines – *join caving club*.

Always take food/warm clothing/helmets/boots with commando soles/good lights/spare candles/spare matches/spare bulbs/spare batteries.

Leave word with others where you are going. Explore caves in fours (at least). Check chances of heavy rainfall. Don't be over-ambitious. Don't underrate danger.

Too
High

10 Too High

Leaping from a railway bridge on to a rocketing train roof may be the prerogative of the film stunt man, and whizzing down a rope from a helicopter the speciality of a Marine Commando – but you can master their basic principles of descent.

Keep cool when too high for comfort – on sinking ship/burning housetop/sagging bridge/stuck-fast Big Wheel/seized-up ski lift. If there is no question of staying put for rescue look at choice of ways down.

You may be hundreds of feet up, yet only need to descend a short way to find an easier way of escape. Remember, too, that gravity is on your side and can be tamed/harnessed/tapped/controlled.

How to Get Down

Climb
(*See Too Low page 176.*)

Weakest person goes down first, strongest last – psychologically best order.

1. **Select low-down handgrips.**
2. **Don't look past feet.**
3. **Face outward or sideways descending slopes.**
4. **Turn inwards when going steepens/view scares/ grips get smaller/footholds may snap (flame-licked staircase say).**

Use make-do rope if available. Strongest man pays it out from top for each person down with the back-rubbing method (*opposite sequence to climbing up*). Then he follows down by . . .

(a) Climbing solo without any aid.

or

(b) Has someone below taking in his rope (tied round his waist by bowline) round that person's back, so that if he does fall on his way down the bottom man will field him if there is still a lot of space below (presuming bottom man is well anchored and using back-towelling method).

or

(c) Slides down rope (tied to solid anchor at top) if rope is not going to be needed any more.

(Climbing down is to be preferred to sliding when rope is weak. Rope can be used instead as safety line.)

Slide

Weakest person goes first, strongest last. Make sure any improvised line is tied securely – and reaches.

Use: ropes/torn sheets/blankets/curtains/creepers/ vines/parachute shroud lines/lightning conductor cables/ships cables/bannisters/tree trunks/poles/posts/masts/wire/hawsers (*see Too Low page 181*).

1. **Grip with hands.**
2. **Hug with arms and elbows.**
3. **Hug with thighs/knees/calves/ankles/feet.**
4. **Come down hand over hand when possible.**
5. **Rest whenever feet can stop (say on knots).**
6. **Don't speed.**

A 10m (30ft) slide down knotted sheets is exhausting – so are most forms of sliding. Enlist help of friction as much as possible, rather than using sheer muscle strength.

Extra aids in building-up friction when faced with sliding down:

Rope Grip hard with inner edges of shoes. If strong enough to hold on with hands alone, do this and cross feet so rope is jammed between a heel and an instep. Once feet frictioning on rope, come down hand over hand. *Do not speed* (and scorch hands).

Knotted lines Take weight on knots when reaching them and stand second or two on them. Passing knotted sheets/curtains/blankets through your trouser belt at top helps – allows you to stop at knots (if big enough) and then ease stomach in and continue. Be careful not to get stuck.

Diagonal/wire/rope Get astride. Lie on top. Grip with both hands. *Hang one foot down straight with toe*

Fig 59   Sliding down diagonal rope

pointing at ground as counterweight. Put other foot up behind and hook toe over wire. Slide slowly hand over hand. *Point toe at ground all way* (it helps to pad chest/stomach/crutch with sweaters and stop rope burn). This works on horizontal ropes, too.

Poles/tree trunks/posts/pipes Bear-hug with arms and elbows. Wrap knees round. Bring ankles and toes back on your side. You can generate more braking friction than seems possible when diameter not too thick.

Long strong rope If rope long enough to reach safety doubled, use as shown (known as abseil to mountaineers; Indian Rope Trick to U.S. Marines).

Place looped end of doubled rope round strong anchor (bed/boulder/tree). Tie loose ends with an overhand knot and lower to ground/ledge/platform/balcony. Check it reaches.

Pass doubled rope between legs and round right leg (*as if towelling back of thigh*) then up across chest and over left shoulder and down into right hand (*as though towelling left shoulder*). Grasp rope in front with left hand. Left-handers should go other way round.

(**Note: right hand brakes your progress when you move it and rope into centre of body.**)

Fig 60   Abseil

Walk backwards down face leaning out. Plant feet flat on surface. Keep legs apart. You will have to push down against friction from rope. Don't try to hold/grip/brake all in one go by tightening that *left* hand – the *right one* is the checking hand.

Let friction do the work. Literally harness it.

When at bottom and no one else to come pull one end of rope s-t-e-a-d-i-l-y so it all comes down and you can use again (if need be). Undo knot first.

(Note: anyone can use this method safely if they have time to practise putting rope on and walking backwards first on flat ground. Trickiest/riskiest part is first few feet off the ledge. Everyone should encourage and help slider to lean away from side in those few feet.)

Remember (mnemonically) . . .

1. **Keep towelling back of right thigh.**
2. **And towel top of left shoulder.**
3. **And brake with right hand.**

Climb-and-slide

Snow slope descent often starts with climbing – and ends by sliding.

Start by climbing down easy-angled/softish snow facing out with legs straight – goosestepping. Plunge heels in. If slope feels too steep, face in to it and kick/hack/scrape handgrips and foosteps in zig-zags. (*Whichever way you start down grasp a stabber-cum-ice pick improvised from keys/rock/wheel brace/hammer/screwdriver/ branch/stick ready for a fall*).

When sliding down snow –

1. **Roll over on to face.**
2. **Bring stabber up to chest.**
3. **Force it into snow gradually with weight of body.**

Thus, the family man struggling up moorland ravine's Eiger-like face after his car has slid off road in midwinter can safety himself to top with wheelbrace.

Fig 61   How a climber or hill walker uses an ice axe to self-arrest a fall down steep snow — the position to go for with any make-do snow stabber

(Avoid avalanche dangers – *see Too Fast page 223*. Avoid hard snow/ice. Take tremendous care if you must come down a snow slope you have never seen before. It could hide hidden drops. Sliding down at speed is equivalent to rushing downstairs in a ruined building in pitch dark.)

Jump

Leap only when flames are licking/roof is falling/deck is disappearing/sands are running out. And then don't hesitate – take deep breath and go.

Weakest jumps first, strongest last.

You can do much to lessen impact *before* jumping. Forget about parachute rolls/cannoball rolls/ breakfalls. Paunchy/past-it/paralytic you can take much more realistic measures.

If you cannot avoid jumping . . .

1. **Try to shorten jump.**
2. **Try to soften landing.**
3. **Try to cage skull.**

Example: *you* are in a bedroom 10m (30ft) from ground. Leap from window and you roar into the deck at about 48 k.p.h. (30 m.p.h.) – a horrifying speed.

> *Shorten* jump by tying the two sheets in room together. Tie on pillow case too. (Note: you have no more material to lengthen this safety line.) Anchor one end to bed and drop sheets out of window. They should reach about half way to ground.
> *Soften* landing by dropping mattress/cushions/ carpet directly where you should land. Just a few inches of softness might save your life.
> *Cage skull* with turban-like construction of woolly jumper/vest/toilet-bag-filled-with-sponges. Or best of all motor cycle crash hat.

Now . . . slide down sheets hang at arm's stretch from bottom (lessens drop by 2m/7ft approx.) and bale out for the bottom. Land in a crumpled heap – as likely – and you can get away with it this way.

Always weigh up your landing – vital if you have nothing to throw down first to break the fall.

Car roof is excellent – has saved people, jumping from top storeys of flats. Excellent shock absorber.

Lawns/gravel paths/gardens/shrubs/trees/snow all better than a landing on flat concrete or cobbles or tarmac which can kill even 5m (15ft) distance fallers.

When soft landing still eludes, look for sloping ground which will help transfer vertical force of jump into a horizontal one – and so absorb energy. Remem-

Fig 62   6m (20ft) drop on to slope (the steeper the better)

ber: parachutist about to land is often moving sideways as well as down – a more favourable situation than a straight-down drop.

If you jump on to a slope . . .

1. **Lower body to full arm's stretch on handgrips (lessens drop by 2m/7ft or so).**
2. **Pick spot to land.**
3. **Push away with outside edge of a foot.**
4. **Turn and jump.**
5. **Let knees buckle on landing. Go down . . .**
   . . . somersault down slope, tucking head well in, going limp.
   (Note: 6m/20ft is a long way. People falling only 3m/10ft clear have flattened foot arches. A 6m/20ft drop can be lethal.)

If the deck is flat and rock/stone/concrete hard, a breakfall *may* prevent you totally creasing yourself. The fall is same as shown except for . . .

1. **Hold arms on each side of head (don't clasp hands).**
2. **Bend knees slightly flexing ankles together.**
3. **Bend knees stiffly on impact.**
4. **Pitch over on one side – thigh/side of body/arm.**
5. **Roll over to other side on your back, legs up, arms saving head.**

By distributing shock over big area rather than specific impact point you have greater chance.

Don't die jumping from burning buildings by leaping too soon (as many have). Wait until very last second for rescue (*see Too Hot page 169*). And check if no other possible way down.

Tell people not to jump when they are crying out in panic and are too high. *Implore them not to until they have no choice* (which is rare).

Jumping into water
(*See also Too Wet page 102.*)
Feet first is simplest/safest/best way of jumping from height – weakest person first.

1. **Pick splash point.**

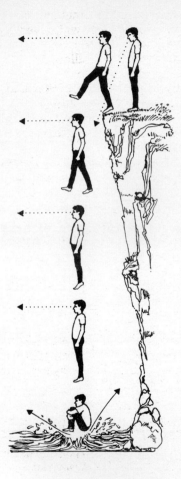

Fig 63   High jump into shallow water

2. **Gaze straight ahead, taking deep breath.**
3. **Stride out with one foot over water.**
4. **Quickly join it with other foot.**
5. **Fall at attention.**
6. **Enter water like toy soldier.**

Avoid circling/spinning/somersaulting in mid-air by never leaning. Try to hit water vertically with feet together, hands on thighs.

   But if water could be shallow . . .

(a) Step well out from side.
(b) Quick breast stroke leg action kick when water comes to waist checks plunge.
(c) Or jump with one leg forwards, one backwards, arms out at side. *And* kick legs together hard when water up to waist.
(d) Or tuck knees to chest with both hands just before impact (flat feet and bottom taking shock).

Falling
(*See also Too Fast page 226.*)

   Fantastic falls (some hundreds of metres) have been survived when fallers –
(a) were drunk/unconscious/dazed.
(b) fell on snow/tree tops/marsh/sloping ground/ water.
(c) made sudden clutch at passing tree/ledge/rope/ chain.
(d) jumped when they realized fall was inevitable. Life doesn't flash back in front of eyes as you drop. You have time to think *maybe a chance*, and to relax/grab/black-out.

Lowering someone else

Only lower injured/aged/young/scared-stiff/uncon-scious if such evacuation *is* necessary.

1. **Check you have somewhere better to lower them to.**
2. **That you already have help there.**

Methods vary and depend on how strong are ropes/ how many helpers to lower/in what state they are/ what kind of person is to be let down.

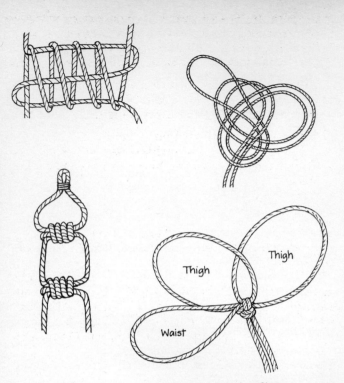

Fig 64   Rope ladder and triple bowline

Tie rope firmly round chest with bowline when only short distance and helpers can manhandle en route.

Remember previous advice on tying your *own* knot if bowline not recollected. Make it a good strong one. *If you know the bowline, triple bowline could prove useful* – say when victim has crushed ribs and cannot be attached by rope round chest.

Use triple bowline knot by tying an ordinary bowline at looped end of a doubled rope (easier to remember than more efficient 'chair' knot) and use the three loops thus produced round person's waist and legs. Adjust for size. So lowered person will not turn upside down loop belt or line under armpits and tie to lowering rope with friction knot. Or thread lowering rope up inside person's buttoned-up coat. Manhandle where possible, on the way.

(Important – don't try lowering more than needed. Risks of losing people too great through limitations of make-do ropes/improvised techniques/ human element/precariousness of position.)

Look for best way to lower away. Don't launch unconscious person out of window of burning building when you could drag downstairs thus:

1. **Roll person on to back on floor.**
2. **Tie wrists with handkerchiefs/tie/shoelaces.**
3. **Kneel astride and loop bound wrists over your neck.**
4. **Crawl to top of stairs.**
5. **Dump person's head at edge of top step.**

Now wriggle clear of bound wrists. Back down stairs gripping your load under armpits, head resting in bend of your arm.

Prevent crashing through fire-weakened stair treads in burning house by not stepping down centre of stairs/keeping to the sides/feeling each tread below with foot first before committing yourself to it.

Remember – handrail could be weakened/too hot to touch/partly missing.

When to Stay Put

When there are plenty of chances of getting help – even though not immediately obvious. On seaside cliff ledge at Bank Holiday. By window with inferno still three floors below. (*See Too Hot page 169.*) . . .

Example: *you* are on a stuck-fast ski chairlift (reasonably rare predicament). Help is obviously near (lift operators within sight). So don't meddle/fiddle/fidget or jump. This causes danger – anything that bounces cable will lead to general panic (whiplash effect jolts all chairs violently).

Sit still, swear if you must, but keep cool (which won't be hard to do over snow slopes – *see Too Cold page 136*).

Many other situations can be saved, when you have time, by the same thing – *thought*.

Meanwhile – *be thinking/checking/probing avenues of escape for when all else fails*.

Height Hazards

Vertigo

Few people suffer dizziness/giddiness/fear of heights/ urge to chuck themselves off to the extent they think.

1. **Encourage and reassure such people** (unless hysterical, in which case appear indifferent and *not* sympathetic).
2. **Only slap face of hysteria-struck as last resort.** And for people so afflicted –

1. **Don't look down** (have companions position your feet).
2. **Take deep breaths.**
3. **Get on with it.**

Bend head of someone suffering uncontrollably from whirling/tilting/fainting vertigo down between knees for short spell. Cold air and water-splashing helps stop fainting.

Vertigo-faint case should be laid on back with feet higher than head (*never* sitting). Loosen clothing. Spatter face/chest with cold water. Rub limbs towards heart. Keep warm on recovery.

Loop or strap victim to some anchor on small ledge so he cannot roll/slip/fling himself off.

Falls
(*See Too Fast page 226.*)

Suicide
High up is best place would-be suicide can draw attention to his predicament. That person out on edge of space and threatening to fall is mentally very distressed. He may appear withdrawn or hostile.

Telephone 999. If not possible don't make sudden act to precipitate person to jump. Sympathetic handling may get response. Don't be manoeuvred into a position (from where you hope to help) where you could be taken down too if person jumps.

Remember – survival is saving your *own* skin. Play the egg-shoving cuckoo by all means, but don't let anyone bring you down too.

Altitude sickness

Caused by lack of oxygen at heights in unacclimatized victim – say at 3,000m (10,000ft) on mountain. Breathlessness/headache/sickness. Acclimatization is answer. Go down. After a day or two's rest victim may be able to ascend gradually.

Phlebitis

Blood can clot at high altitude. **Signs:** pain and swelling in lower legs and abdomen. **Danger:** clot could break loose and lodge in lung. **Prevention:** beware of inactivity which can make blood sludge in veins of leg or lower abdomen – when resting raise painful leg frequently, exercise all leg muscles vigorously, rotate ankles once an hour.

Mountain Emergencies

Get down into valleys when lost/exhausted/bad weather coming/night drawing in. Don't make bones about it – *get down*.

If too dark and/or terrain is too rugged to descend, then bivouac for night (*see Too Cold page 140*).

Finding way off

(a) Don't follow water downhill nor the gorges/ravines/waterfalls/canyons/ghylls it carves.
(b) Don't enter gully fissures between rock faces.
(c) Don't rush downhill = many unseen dangers.
> *Sudden cliff drops*
> *Treacherous shale slopes*
> *Slippery grass*
> *Boulder fields*
(d) Beware of cornices (snow overhangs). Invisible when walking above them on mountain skyline, you might tread on them and burst through (having led others into same trap).

Prevention: always walk well to windward side of mountain ridge/skyline/horizon/edge rather than towards sheltered side.

When an accident happens

1. Make sure everyone in party is safe.

2. **Get casualty to safest place even if you have to carry unless you suspect spine injury** (*see Too Fast page 226*).
3. **Keep warm and render first-aid.**
4. **Messengers go for help** (*see Too Lonely page 25*).
5. **Remaining companions build shelter/keep up casualty's warmth and morale/signal help.**

Prevention When going mountain climbing, join climbing club in your district – address from library.

Always take warm clothing/spare food/properly soled boots/torch/compass/map/whistle/spare sweaters.

Leave word with others where you are going. But check chances of bad weather first. Don't be over-ambitious. Never underrate danger.

Too
Fast

11 Too Fast

Any speed is fast enough to kill when the unexpected happens. Mesmerized as you approach collision-point – whether at 15 or 150 k.p.h. (10 or 100 m.p.h.) – what you should do to survive and actually *do* do are very different things.

Careering across central reservation of motorway or tumbling in an avalanche only chaos prevails: those without an earthly sometimes escape while someone else with every chance dies. And vice versa.

There is no set law – save anticipating things going too fast with you on board by (1) preparing ahead by always wearing a seat belt and (2) knowing the best you can do when totally unprotected (given presence of mind to act in time).

Car Crash
Fitting seat belts – and wearing them – is now compulsory by law in Britain and in many other countries. Yet it is still possible that you might have to travel in a belt-less car. Or some *similar* vehicle. Anywhere. Any time. Possibly at speed.

Given time to think, fast reactions you can do *something* as crash approaches a second or two away. Car driver braced so savagely on steering wheel in 130 k.p.h. (80 m.p.h.) crash (in expensive car) that his grip twisted steering wheel – and he escaped: girl driver leaped into back of sports car as crash loomed ahead – and lived. Such instances are very much exceptions to the general rule – that a car crash = virtually inevitable injury or death.

It is impossible to be dogmatic about beltless crash survival. But following points *may* help you survive as they have others (and are backed up by motoring authorities as scientifically realistic).

Pre-collision action when not strapped in for head-on crash

1. **Do opposite of natural instinct to push away from crash.**
2. **Fling yourself towards point of impact . . .**
3. **Wrapping arms round head . . .**
4. **Twisting sideways and lying across front with flank.**

If driving, hold steering wheel tightly. Aim to get car out of as much trouble as possible. Moving head against steering wheel at crash moment has worked (but controversial measure in view of those steering columns which 'always' spear straight back towards rear window in old-fashioned vehicle).

Back seat passengers lie (as above) against back of front seats.

This is very much a last-stand tactic. Usually there is no time to think. But with two or three seconds warning, quick reaction and knowing right thing to do you can take advantage this way of energy-absorbing capability of car as bonnet crumples in head-on crash.

Never sit back and try to brace from oncoming crunch. No matter how well braced you are, first the car will stop (say at 50 k.p.h./ 30 m.p.h. to zero in 60cm/2ft). And then you, still travelling at pre-accident speed, will have second collision with car's windscreen/rail/scuttle/door surrounds/dash/steering column/seats in front.

Going with car from very beginning heightens your chances. Technically – object of surviving crash once it is determined to happen, is to get passengers to lose their speed over greatest possible distance and hence reduce to absolute minimum the deceleration to which they are subjected.

Non-technically: *go with it* (most serious impact accidents happen at combined speeds of less than 65 k.p.h. (40 m.p.h.).

When driver is drunk/suicidal/tearaway
If very good chance car is soon going to crash, and driver is acting fantastically irresponsibly, protect yourself.

1. **Feign sickness and vomiting all over car interior to make him stop then whip out ignition key.**

if no joy here . . .

2. Lie on floor in back of car if possible.
3. Or lie braced against front of car.

(Note: climbing into back from front seat so you can get down on floor might distract and make drunk or suicidal driver lose control.)

Switching off and pulling out ignition key while car is travelling has worked – obviously last resort. Dangerous.

Make sure you have clear/straight/wide road stretch. Take a firm grip of wheel (after noting where handbrake is) as you reach across to turn and pull out key. Easier to do this – by virtue of key position – in some cars than in others.

Important: realize that steering car with hand on steering wheel while seated in passenger seat is very very tricky. And a last resort.

When brakes go
Change down. Pull on handbrake. If still no use . . .

Drive off road. Keep repeating if you bounce out until stopped.

If not possible to drive straight off road, brush against side of road (walls/banks/buildings, to give slowing effect). Don't think about ruining vehicle – think about surviving.

Brace as best you can if crash comes.

Action when skidding
Driver should try to reduce the steering angle of car.

If front wheels have lost their grip, a smaller steering angle can help regain control by completing a wider turn than was intended. Trying to sharpen the turn will aggravate the skid more – so will braking.

If back wheels slide, say to left, and car starts spinning to the right, turn steering wheel to left very briefly. This is natural way, but it must be instant and not violent.

Over-correction of skids is common – due to steering wheel being yanked too far over and for too long. Only way to cope with skiddy surfaces is slow down and drive steadily.

When taxed to your limit on a bend watch outside verge for only true indication of its sharpness.

Preventing skidding
Basically when roads are not dry:

1. **Brake on straight, not on bends.**
2. **Drive much slower than on dry roads.**
3. **Leave extra room between you and vehicle ahead.**
4. **Brake gently. Don't steer forcefully.**

Special hazards are: fog, strong winds, rain; darkness as well as conditions on the road surface. For example, overtaking lorry in clear patch on misty road could run you head-on into wall of fog again during passing-time, with real skid-risk on damp surface.

Cutting speed on wet road – especially with worn tyres – necessary. At 80 k.p.h. (50 m.p.h.) in rain your car surfs along with tyres off the road on a wedge of water. Even with reasonable tyre tread, car is partly out of contact with road for same reason at 95 k.p.h. (60 m.p.h.)

Slow down well ahead of hazard points:

> Roundabouts
> Bends
> Steep hills
> Junctions
> Obstacles/diversions/emergency signs.

Read road surfaces between the lines – certain skiddy surfaces are not always obvious. Rough/gravelly/knobbly surface could prove skiddiest of any. Summer roads after rain shower often more skiddy than same road after rain in winter.

Lightness in steering is good warning sign generally.

Have your steering and brakes garage-tested all round frequently. Inspect tyres often. There must be at least 1mm of tread for three-quarters of the width of the tyre, the remaining quarter of the tyre having a visible pattern. Check with a 5p coin. If the inner edge of the raised rim of the coin is still in view when inserted into the tread it is time to renew the tyre.

(Note: fast motoring is made safer by increasing tyre pressure as makers recommend.)

Overtaking safely

Overtaking means speed. And risk of escalating chaos. Think hard before you judge whether to pull out and increase speed, or stay put.

1. **Don't close up on car in front.**
2. **Don't worry about anyone jumping into that gap.**
3. **Assess any hazards ahead from your superior road position.**

Keeping your distance behind vehicle to be overtaken means you don't blind/mask/shade your vital view ahead. Keep two car lengths behind at 40 k.p.h. (25 m.p.h.) and eight lengths at 95 k.p.h (60 m.p.h). This gives adequate sight of road ahead, bends, junctions, corners, obstructions forcing vehicle in front to pull out suddenly, oncoming traffic.

Check in rear mirror for queue jumper coming up behind, but don't let this force you to close that gap between you and vehicle in front. When ready to overtake you will be the one to go first.

When it is time to pass . . . in quick succession:

4. **Check rear mirror.**
5. **Pull out and accelerate in gear which will let you pass fast without having to change gear.**
6. **Touch horn.**
7. **If other car accelerates, drop back.**

A car in front doing 95 k.p.h. (60 m.p.h.) needs your doing 110 k.p.h. (70 m.p.h.) to pass – and you must ensure you don't have to cut in immediately afterwards. Drop back if this looks probable.

Seat Belts for Survival

Seat belts definitely reduce risk of death or maiming by as much as 70%. Examples of ways seat belts save . . .

(a) Stop you being thrown from car, almost certain cause of death or injury (locking doors often fails as crash distorts bodywork and door flies open).
(b) Stop head being done in on screen rail/scuttle/door surrounds.
(c) Stop face being cut on bits of broken windscreen.
(d) Stop chest and intestines being smashed on dash

or scuttle or (usually) steering column for driver. *Always wear a seat belt even for short journeys.*

Saving children

Buy seat and harness for child under 36kg (80lbs). Fit to back seat. If over 36kg (80lbs) child can use adult harness on back seat.

Children should always sit in the back (whether strapped in or not). Doors should have child-proof locks. Ways to get them to wear the harness: tell them car won't start until they do/they're astronauts going to moon/they'd better hurry up, or else.

Never allow:

Children to sit on front passenger's seat.
Child to sit on mother's knee in front.
Child to be tucked between mother and her seat belt.

Carricots are best placed on floor in the back between back seat and front seats. If no room place it on back seat and secure with strong net.

After the Crash

Control other road-users by signalling (get help from other motorists and onlookers). In fog, darkness, rain and twisty road especially, light flare (oily rags burning inside levered-off hub caps) placed some way from wreck to warn others.

Only move someone badly hurt if danger of fire from spilled petrol (no one should smoke) or if danger from traffic cannot be avoided. Treat for injuries (see later). But where casualty must be moved handle *very* carefully, especially if broken bones suspected or complaint of pain in back (spinal injury-risk).

Motor Cycle Crash

Out of the very little you can do in bike crash salvage these key points:

1. **Get rid of bike immediately crash is certain.**
2. **Fall limp, tucking head in.**
3. **Try to roll into a ball.**

But most survival measures should have been taken in advance.

4. **Be wearing best crash helmet available when solo.**
5. **Be wearing best crash helmet available when pillion.**

In heat of moment you can do very little without practice in doing neck rolls, cannonball somersaults and 'relaxed' falling. Every tumble is different. Once you are flying through air at 95 k.p.h. (60 m.p.h.) you have no time to modify action.

It is essential to fall limp – without arms and legs sticking out.

And to fight against instinct to ride the bike out – motor-cyclists with 1000cc BMW machine or moped run on a shoestring never like to abandon ship even in direst crisis. But you must.

Train Crash

Don't think you haven't an earthly in a train crash (rare as they happen). You may have several seconds warning as carriages cavort to standstill. Further – trains differ the world over, possibly giving you more chance in one situation than another. And where any advance knowledge could save your life.

In the compartment
As train lurches/rocks/careers, and if time to act:

1. **Fling yourself flat on floor.**
2. **Clasp back of neck, face down.**
3. **Wait for it.**

Quick reaction in doing this means best survival position against twisted metal/flying suitcases/spraying glass. How you fare in full compartment depends on your reactions. Get down fast – and first.

Passengers with back to engine too late to hit the floor should clasp back of neck with hands neverthe-less. And brace.

In corridor
Throw yourself on the floor . . .

1. **On back, feet to engine.**

2. **Hands clasped behind neck.**
3. **Feet pushing against anything solid, knees bent.**

In toilet/lavatory/w.c.

If time to act forget about wiping bottom/pulling up pants/drying hands. Fling yourself into action . . .

1. **Sit on floor with back to engine.**
2. **Bend knees.**
3. **Clasp hands behind neck.**
4. **Brace (and hope cubicle is crushproof).**

In sleeper

Be asleep – and relaxed: key factor in crash/collision/impact survival.

Outside the train

You can help prevent train crashes by signalling any train approaching crash/car-stuck-on-level-crossing/debris-strewed-by-vandals-on-railway-track and so on.

Recognized stop signal on railways, when no red light or red flag available, is to face oncoming train from safe position and raise both hands vertically above head.

At night: violently swing light (any colour) from side to side as train approaches.

When you see obstructions dropped/thrown/placed across lines let railway authorities know immediately. If you know train is due any minute (through local knowledge, signals or sound in distance) and you feel you have chance to shift it, then do so after quickly weighing up danger to yourself and others.

Once on the track (and trespassing) you might be surprised by any oncoming train and not know which lines it is running on. Especially as no reliable indication from the tracks as to which way they are worked.

Don't attempt to lie between the running rails (where there are sleepers) but fling yourself flat in space between two adjacent tracks.

(Note: where ground level electrification is used, conductor rails must be avoided.)

Plane crash

Take-off and landing are crisis points. Once in the air and emergency happens, pilot can do wonders.

Ditchings happen when there is no panic – everyone following crew's directions.

A cause for panic can be sudden lurch in mid-flight (possibly pilot taking evasive action, or turbulence) when without warning passengers are shaken. Only remedy for this is to be ready for it or wear seat belt for most of time.

Before any emergency (when you will be briefed exactly what to do) once you are flying, read survival instruction card or booklet placed in front of you.

This will tell best position to brace in impact. Variations differ between airlines. Generally it is:

Seat belt fastened tight
Chair fully upright
Bend forward with one arm across knees
Place pillow on lap and hold head on pillow with other arm
Push and brace legs forward
You will be warned when to brace

Tall people not having room should push backrest of seat in front forward and rest folded arms on it, holding their head firmly. But there are variations to these bracing positions – depending on airline and instructions in front of you.

When descending over water: loosen collar and tie, remove spectacles, false teeth, sharp or breakable objects and high-heeled shoes. Take up impact position and *brace* when told by the crew (*see Too Wet page 95*) until you stop. Wait for second impact as the nose hits the water.

In planes where you are *not* sitting in airliner-type accommodation ditching positions are . . .
(a) Brace back against bulkhead, facing towards tail. Bend knees and grasp hands at base of skull to protect neck.
(b) Sit in seats if (1) near emergency exits (2) got harnessing which may be burst-proof. Seats facing aft best. If facing forward brace as near position given above as possible.

(c) If (a) or (b) impossible lie braced across the floor of
     plane, or . . .
(d) Flat on floor, feet forward and bent at knees –
     braced against anything solid.
In each case *stay braced until aircraft stops.*

(Note: if possible whip off collar/tie/etc. first – see
above.)

Falling Lifts

It is essential no part of body touches floor at impact.

Many lifts have a ledge like a picture rail on their
side walls just below roof. Jump and cling on this
desperately so as to raise body from floor. Older
passengers (or in ledgeless lift) should try jumping up
and down during time the lift falls so they may be off
the floor on impact.

(Note: all modern passenger lifts have safety gear
which makes this eventuality very unlikely. Worst
condition most likely is lift car over-travelling bottom
terminal floor and striking buffers in lift pit.)

Avalanches

Never give up in terror of an avalanche: keep fighting.
It can happen on any steep hillside where fresh new
snow up to three days old (or possibly longer) lies on
old hard snow, and where, if you break the surface
tension, it all rushes down like a pack of cards.

This is prevalent in gullies.

Signs are new snow. Thaw conditions (sun/rain/
heat). Snowballs rolling downhill. Remember – one
avalanche could follow another very quickly striking
in quick succession. A shout can trigger an avalanche.

Keep away from such areas. If an avalanche slope
has to be crossed try throwing rocks and snowballs
first to see if you can precipitate it.

Anatomy of avalanche is that if you are swept down
by it you will be swallowed underneath quite out of
sight in a matter of seconds.

Once buried under snow you may be able to breathe
if among boulders in the avalanche tip at the bottom.
But as soon as avalanche stops, terrific pressure is

released and the tip freezes concrete-hard immediately – with you entombed inside.

Whole action in avalanche survival is to be in optimum position when this happens.

(a) Have bindings of skis in quick-release position, slacked off in readiness. Take hands out of loops on ski sticks or, if climbing, take off ice axe wrist strap.

(b) Tread lightly on danger zone.

(c) Keep planning what you will do, which way you will try to escape, if avalanche starts.

If slope does avalanche . . . with fracture suddenly snaking across slope with muffled detonation and whole plate of snow peeling away:

1. **Get rid of skis/sticks/ice axe immediately.**
2. **Quickly check if at top/centre/sides or bottom end of fall.**
3. **Dive for best escape at top or sides if possible.**
4. **At all costs try to delay downhill slide.**

This can possibly be done by leaping upwards if avalanche breaks off by ankles. Or to one side if you are near solid snow. Or by clinging to some bush or rock horn sticking out of snow. The less snow above you, the less to bury you later.

5. **Keep mouth shut tightly.**
6. **Swim.**

Try swimming for side. Use sort of double-action back stroke with back to force of avalanche and head up. If in danger of being clobbered by solid slabs of snow try rolling into a ball. There is no cut and dried answer. Ride it out as best you can. But keep your mouth shut (many avalanche victims die from drowning with snow melting into lungs).

7. **Reserve greatest effort for last few seconds.**
8. **Bring arm up in front of nose and mouth.**
9. **When avalanche stops make one huge effort to break out.**

As avalanche loses momentum and starts to settle two things are paramount: an airspace in front of face and being as near as possible to the surface. In that last final effort if you don't know which way up you are, spit. And go in opposite direction to saliva.

Lastly . . .

10. Don't panic when trapped.

Much much easier to say than do. But fear uses oxygen by accelerating breathing rate and you want to save oxygen as much as possible. Try hard to keep calm.

In many avalanche areas rescuers will arrive quickly. Dogs are used more and more and highly efficient at finding survivors. In many cases survivors have lived underground, though completely jammed fast, for hours.

It is possible to shout if near enough to surface to hear people, though unlikely you will be heard by them.

Aids to help searchers: coloured avalanche cord tied round your waist in advance with marks every metre to arrow towards your buried body (you could lie to a loosened coil of rope before you move on to dangerous zone). It will stay on surface if you are buried and lead rescuers to you.

Also – flares with cords attached which fit into ski sticks. Special bootpolish for aiding dogs. Magnets in boots help searchers with mine detectors.

There are different kinds of avalanche – wet concrete/dry sugar/crazy paving. You may land nearer surface in wet snow than in powder. If avalanche is broken slabs, jump on top and toboggan.

Best preventive action: go on avalanche course at outdoor pursuits centre – and learn how to dig snow pit in slope and 'read' the condition of layers of old snow revealed below – for that particular day.

Speed Hazards (including falls)

Shock *see Too Lonely page 33.*
Bleeding
Unconsciousness } *see Too Crowded page 62.*
Broken bones
Breathing stopped *see Too Wet page 105.*

Don't move anyone injured by violence if at all possible. Dragging inert body from wrecked lorry/train/car could kill if human frame is broken-up inside or spine is fractured.

Never stuff unconscious/bleeding/deformed accident victim into car and race to hospital. Wait for medical help to come to them . . . in meantime do everything to get help/stop bleeding/keep patient warm and treating for shock.

If you *have* to move victim (say because of flood/ falling rocks/fire) – *see Too Slow page 239.*

Broken spine
Movement or pressure on spinal cord will cause paralysis – hence need for *not* moving injured.

Persons likely to complain they cannot feel legs/legs and feet are numb/feel body cut in two. Pain in back and neck possible too.

Slack off clothing at waist and neck. Warn injured not to move at all. Don't give anything to drink. Never raise head. Keep warm/stop bleeding/treat burns – but don't move for examination.

Too
Slow

12   Too Slow

The castaway who decides or is forced to move out from desert island/ditched plane/marooned car rather than wait for rescue is chancing his arm against big odds.

This is the classic situation where many have left stranded transport to walk out, and few have been seen alive again. Circumstances vary greatly, according to whether the trip is over sand/snow/ice, through jungle or by water.

The decision to travel instead of wait is critical. Judgment here counts as much as doggedness later. Look at all the factors collectively, never singly. Look at all the factors collectively, never singly.

When You Become Stranded

1. **Ensure everyone is safe.**
2. **Apply first-aid.**
3. **Make shelter/check water/light fire.**
4. **Place signalling equipment ready.**
5. **Relax.**
6. **Make plan of action.**

When to Move Out

Stay with or near wrecked transport whenever possible. It is seen more easily from the air, gives shade/shelter/materials, offers supply of oil/petrol/water, and radio. You save energy.

Often the decision is taken out of your hands when crew of ditched plane/shipwreck/stranded coach are there to make it for you.

But travel is often best for the solo castaway – motorist/sailor/pilot – if there is a possible way out. Decision here is: how long to stay with immobile transport before trekking out?

There are various factors (*see Too Lonely page 17*).

(a) Have you given up all reasonable hope of rescue?
(b) Do you know way to civilization?
(c) Are you fit to travel?
(c) Are you certain you can make it?

If you answer 'Yes' each time, start planning to move out.

Preparing to Travel

Don't rush. Pack carefully. Relax and sleep as much as possible before leaving. Test and adjust improvised equipment before accepting it.

Maps
You must know where you are heading. If you have no map, draw one of surroundings and distant landmarks. Add to it as you travel to prevent walking in a circle.

Make map case from parachute material/clothing/plastic. Don't pack it away with rest of gear, but slip it down shirt front, or keep in a pocket.

Copy map by shading on its back with pencil/charcoal/crayon, then press this side down on paper or cardboard and stencil through by drawing over original map.

There are many substitutes for paper: tin/inner birch bark/shirt tail.

Compass
Besides personal compass, or those in aircraft survival packs, retrieve any car/boat/plane compass (remove any compensating magnets).

Allow for magnetic variations as shown on maps.

Don't use compass near metal objects or camera exposure meters. Check compass often with night sky.

Rucksack
Wrap everything in groundsheet/polythene sheet/coat. Strap this to readymade pack frame (as shown) which can be lashed together from almost anything rigid. Pad with foam or kapok (from vehicle seats or spare clothing) to protect your back.

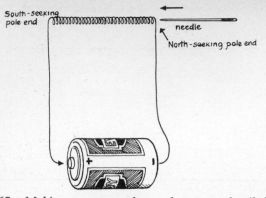

*Fig 65   Making a compass from a battery and coiled wire
and needle*

*Wire should be enamelled so that turns don't short out each
other (as happens with copper wire). Many turns of wire are
needed – overlapping in layers. Coil should be wound closely,
yet loosely, on pin or needle. Test needle by hanging on a
thread or floating on water on a leaf (take leaf away and
needle will still float on water's skin – and rotate too).*

Make a small ledge at bottom of the frame to prevent
load slipping lower or improvise a hip belt to take most
of the load on the hips rather than the shoulders.

Don't carry more than 14kg (30lbs).

Practise using a headband (broad cloth band for
forehead tied to frame top with cord) which lifts the
pack frame off the shoulders.

Practise packing with what is to be carried:

*Matches/lighter/
firelighters (keep dry)
Water
Food
Map and compass
(best in clothing or pocket)
Signalling mirror
(best in safe pocket)
Watch (best worn)
Petrol/oil/paraffin bottle
(keep away from food)
Knife*

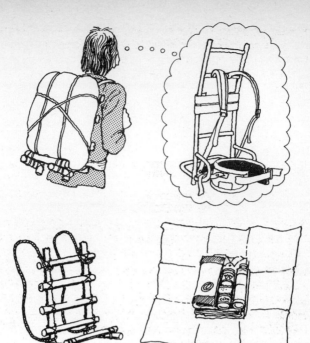

Fig 66 Pack frame and improvised version with hip belt

> *Torch*
> *Spare clothes*
> *Shelter material*
> *Gun and ammunition*
> *First-aid kit*

Footwear

Wear shoes. Repair or make new ones from tyre rubber/parachute fabric/animal hide. Anything that can give a strong sole and soft uppers.

Wear layers of material inside shoes to insulate feet. Lace up outer covers with improvised thongs.

(a) Sandals are simple to make for desert travel – just tough soles and fabric straps.

(b) Skis improvised from wood or metal vehicle parts should not be longer than 1m (3ft) and be about 15cm (6in) wide. Make ski sticks from branches.

(c) Snow shoes can be made from forked spruce or

willow limbs. Tie interwoven branches in place. Or use metal tubing/wood panels/wire mesh – anything to spread your load on snow.

Clothing

Unless very cold, carry most clothing in pack rather than wear it. Wear sufficient for weather/insect/sun protection.

Don't jettison it. Spare clothing means shelter, bedding, bandages, tinder, string, and signalling gear. And more.

Survival transport

Avoid load-carrying whenever possible. Use whatever form of transport you can make or patch-up to save your energy.

Sledge

Use vehicle doors/cowlings/seat runners. Planks or branches. Even parachute and dinghy material. Anything that slides and carries.

A single tow line with individual shoulder loops is generally best. On risky ice, however, it may be safer to have several towlines attached so that you can all use different footholds, not just follow one trail-breaker (as is best on snow).

Tie single towline to sledge bridle (V of rope jutting forward like snowplough).

Small solo sledge can be made for long open snow slopes from balled-up parachute/hub caps/gas cape on spur of moment.

Raft

Don't be optimistic of a river raft carrying you and your possessions without adjustment first. Example: a raft floating on two 45 litre (10 gallon) oil drums only just about supports a man not weighing more than 78 kg (13 stones) and its own weight.

Wood is an excellent float. *But* . . .

1. **Use light-woods**
2. **Test floating quality of each log first.**
3. **Don't use large trees.**

Raft 2m (6ft) wide made from logs about 15cm (6in) in diameter and 3–4m (10–12ft) long is a useful one-man size. Buoyancy can be supplemented by anything else that floats well.

(a) Fix buoyancy round edges rather than in the centre.

(b) Add far more buoyancy than you need to carry the intended weight of passengers and gear.

(c) Don't build square rafts. Pointed rafts easiest to propel. Rectangular, best general design.

(d) Use parachute shroud lines/wire/vines for lashings. Strap buoyancy floats very tightly.

(e) Oil drums are best lashed longwise between parallel poles.

(f) A logs-only raft should have a platform of thinner logs on top, but majority of poles should be in bottom layer.

Bamboo rafts are easy/light/quick rafts to make if you find some bamboo.

(g) Pans/buckets/bottles add buoyancy to raft. So do reeds or straw carefully packed dry in a groundsheet (but ensure folds of sheet come above waterlevel) – lash this to raft like oil drum.

(h) Square sail will power pointed-nosed raft (more or less downwind).

Punt raft on shallow water with pole (preferably with forked end). Deep water means rowing or paddling with flat end of a branch or flat object nailed or jammed on to pole (say pan lid).

Coracle

Make framework by sticking green saplings in a circle in the ground, then bending them over and lashing together as if frame for *flat-roofed* igloo (place rock on top).

Weave in sidepieces till structure is robust. Then pull out of ground, turn over, add saplings round edge to form gunwhale. Flat bottom is important.

Cover tautly with plastic sheet/tarpaulin/groundsheet. Paddle it by oar. Practise a lot first in shallows.

Emergency dinghy

Inflatable dinghy from aircraft and boats must be properly inflated. Top up with pump/bellows/

blowing. Avoid over-inflation. Leave seat uninflated if injured people lying down.

Close valves tight. Check inflation regularly. Release air when hot; add air when cold. Leaks most likely underwater, along seams and at valves. Use repair plugs provided.

Rig canopy/curtain/awning if sea is rough (depending on type of raft).

When foraging among floating wreckage on sea don't drag in sharp metal objects carelessly.

Try to obtain a parachute pack before wreck goes down and you take to dinghy.

Always stream a sea anchor over the side (make from bucket/garbage/cloth-ball if proper drogue missing) so you don't drift far from wrecksite.

Don't let sea anchor rope chafe raft.

Car or van

Bogged, ditched or broken-down transport is not necessarily the end if you are involved in a race for life – whether in desert or deserted countryside.

Techniques for getting moving again will depend on your mechanical knowledge. Here are some very basic examples.

(a) When wheel stuck in ditch: three men can usually bounce car out without help from engine. Lift bumper, gain up and down momentum and bounce wheel out sideways. If only two people – one should drive, one bounce. Avoid wheel spin. Drive car out at angle it went in.

(b) Stuck in slush/mud/ice: don't race engine. Engage first gear and drive with absolute minimum of throttle so wheels crawl out. Add weight above driving wheels.

(c) If in ruts, try easing car forward then whip out clutch so it rolls back, then go forward again, then back and so on to build up momentum to climb out.

A scarf or belt tied round tyre (through slots in wheel) will often 'bump' car out of ruts as you drive.

Hefty passengers rocking car at the back works. Lift as high as possible, let car roll back then build up momentum again until final heave clears it.

Starter motor can get you out (although it throws heavy strain on battery): take out plugs and use starter motor with bottom or reverse gear.

Drive out in straight line with rear-wheel-driven car, but turning steering wheel quickly if front-wheel-drive helps gain grip.

(d) Deep ruts mean a combination of digging and possibly using jack to lift wheels clear so you can place planks/branches/stones underneath.

Use everything to help wheels grip – even dirt scraped from underneath wings, floormats and sacking (they might be tossed out by wheels but worth trying).

There have been many improvisations to get transport moving at all costs. Rope wrapped round wheel has served as tyre. Whisky/paraffin/coconut-oil-mixed-with-high-octane petrol have all served as fuel.

These examples show what can be done with contents of a woman's handbag:

Nylon stocking (reef-knotted) substitutes for broken fan belt.

Hairpin or silver paper mends blown vehicle fuse.

Nail varnish stops wire shorting on metal bodywork.

Nail file makes screwdriver and sparking plug point adjuster.

Plastic rainhood binds split radiator hose (tie with belt).

Face powder seals leaking radiator.

More drastic measures may be needed: weigh up rapidly whether the risks justify doing possible serious damage to vehicle or whether you must get transport moving without fail.

Direction Finding

You should have some idea where you are before setting out (though to be accurate you need compass, sextant, watch and accurate navigation tables if you are suddenly pitched into wilderness).

Direction without compass
North Star and Southern Cross (*see Too Dark page 127*) will always show north and south – when you can see them.

Also the sun rises approximately in the east and sets roughly in the west.

There are three daytime methods of finding direction.

(a) Stick pole upright in flat ground. Starting in the morning mark a point at the top of the pole's shadow about every hour (you don't need a watch). At end of day draw a line connecting points and it will run east-west. Shortest distance from pole's base to this line is north-south.

(Note: in northern hemisphere base of pole will point south and the other end north and vice versa in southern hemisphere.)

(b) If your watch has correct local time, shadow of an upright stick at 1200 will point north-south. Remember which hemisphere you are in as with (a).

(c) Point hour hand of watch (with right local time) at the sun. Midway between the hand and 12 o'clock will be a line pointing south (if in northern hemisphere). Method is not accurate when sun is very high. Draw dial/hands if watch is digital.

(Note: hold piece of grass vertically to cast shadow across dial and line up hour hand with this shadow.)

You can still get general idea of where the sun is even on dark or overcast day (*see Too Dark page 127*).

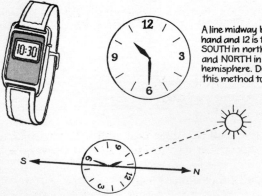

A line midway between hour hand and 12 is taken as SOUTH in northern hemisphere and NORTH in southern hemisphere. Don't rely on this method too much.

Fig 67   Translating direction from a quartz digital watch in southern hemisphere (via a quick sketch)

Try more than one method to check direction. Once you have found it keep it.

Keeping on route without compass

Pick two obvious distant objects exactly on the line of travel. Walk to the first then, before reaching the second, pick another far landmark still dead-on line. Keep in line as you walk.

Remember them when you stop. Rest facing in direction of travel. Draw arrow in ground. Or build rock pointer.

Distances are deceptive. Multiply estimated distances by three. View distance you are covering pessimistically. Reckon on 3 k.p.h. (2 m.p.h.) for straightforward walking conditions.

Be prepared to detour (as you would with a compass) at obstacles like dense thickets/cliffs/swamps. Calculate carefully where your detour will bring you back on course again at the far side if possible.

Fill in map as you go along to check you are not curving away from destination in a wide circle.

Blaze a trail. Use rocks/branches/debris to make your route clear for anyone following, or if you have to backtrack.

Slash tree trunks with knife/rock/sharp instrument to make a white flash about chest-level (so you spot them easily when backtracking, even if snowing).

If you get lost

When separated from (and out of sound of) companions . . .

1. **Don't panic.**
2. **Stop.**
3. **Sit down and think back.**
4. **Signpost where you are.**
5. **Try to find trail again.**

Return to site you signposted if still unsuccessful. Prepare to bivouac (*see Too Cold page 140*) before nightfall.

Next morning will seem less frightening. Try for a high view – whether from tall tree or hill. Look for companions' smoke (you also have lit a fire).

Draw valleys/streams/hills you see on paper or bark.

Never trust a landscape to memory only.

If you still haven't a clue make in straightest line possible for a known coast. Or follow downsteam of river: even in remotest area, it will eventually lead to habitation. Continue trail blazing.

If you could backtrack successfully along your path in the very beginning you were not really lost.

Walking

Leave big sign for any passing aircraft pointing to way you have started to trek out at the original crash site.

Walk very slowly at first. If sign of blisters stop and treat (*see page 250*). Gradually lengthen pace out to longer stride. Never set blistering pace.

Zig-zag up hills. Walk in single file. Don't crowd each other or race for first place. Weakest person should go first on open slopes and flat country.

Always keep together. If one stops, everyone else should. It is morale raising for someone to go ahead to blaze the route and make camp . . . but don't lose them.

Stop whenever you need to rather than at set periods. But beware of too-frequent stops. Try to keep going for long stretches at an easy pace.

Avoid canyons, cliffs, thickets, swamps when you can skirt them, though it may take you much further out of the chosen way.

Stop in darkness, mist and blizzard. Shelter immediately (*see Too Cold page 140*).

Always stop in good time to prepare camp before darkness.

Negotiate unpassable swamps with pole. If sinking lie flat and roll and wriggle with pole crosswise under shoulders or chest to 'swim' to side. Don't make violent panicky movements.

Keep eating (*see Too Empty page 266*), drinking (*see Too Dry page 72*), and cheerful: sing.

Sledging

Don't be tempted to ride fast down steep slopes on sledge after long session of hauling.

Sit astride small sledge with feet firmly planted on ground. And grasping line at front. Brake by digging in heels and lifting front end of sledge off the ground.

Pick clear route to bottom – well away from trees which are hard to steer through. Keep braking.

Carrying someone injured
Lifting a casualty to a safe place for treatment any-where needs improvisation and patience. There are various methods.
(a) Fireman's lift (as shown).
(b) Two-, three- and four-handed lifts (as shown).
(c) Sheet slid on level floor (as shown).
(d) Coat-and-poles stretcher (as shown).
(e) Rope stretcher – hard to make and carry.
(f) Pick-a-back with victim's feet through a backpack frame (worn on carrier's back): suitable when the injured can hang on to you.

Fig 69   3-handed lift

Fig 68   Fireman's lift

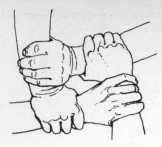

Fig 70   4- and 2-handed lifts

Fig 71   Makeshift stretcher

Fig 72   Drag sheet

240

(g) Same as (f) with injured's feet slipped through coil of rope, coil being worn by carrier like a coat (he first puts one arm through half, then the other and top of coil crosses back of his neck).

(h) Sledge as carrier – don't speed.

(i) Raft carrier – be careful not to capsize.

Don't cripple yourself trying to fireman's lift someone too heavy. You need additional help. Remember principles of lifting – *see Too Lonely page 29*.

When injured is not in desperate-looking condition and *has* to be moved to safety he/she can be carried between two helpers using various hand grips. Three-handed one is variation on two-handed (*see fig 69*) depending on weight/strength/size of injured and helpers. Injured is supported by free hand of one helper.

Four-handed lift can carry injured who is able to hold on to shoulders of two people carrying him between them. Two-hand grip (fig 70) is best for injured not able to help himself at all – and who is then supported by both carriers' spare arms in position roughly as for three-handed lift.

Serious casualties should be moved as little as possible (*see Too Fast page 226*). If essential, however, move on improvised stretcher for patient must be in lying or semi-lying position. Best stretcher is rigid – door/plank/bench. Failing this use jackets and coats threaded on poles as shown.

If possible to drag injured just a short way to safety feed blanket/sheet/tarpaulin underneath (very gently) keeping body in position it already lies.

Remember . . .

1. **Move body lengthways not sideways, and if you have to lift up patient (heaven forbid) then support each part of body and carry it in a straight line . . .**

2. **Never let body sag in centre by just picking up head and feet.**

Water Travel

Crossing rivers
(*See Too Wet page 98*.)

Rafting
Distribute weight over raft evenly. Stand or sit round edges to balance other paddlers. If load slips, balance it on far side immediately while sorting it out.

A sail can be more trouble than it's worth. But if your course is downwind take advantage of it.

Raft travel is very slow. Take it easy. Don't try to hurry. Only sail in daylight. Don't fall asleep. Listen and watch for hazards ahead: spray/noise/silver line across water. Don't enter smooth-walled gorges. Attach a long line so you can let raft down small river rapids from the bank.

Keep near to land. When faced with rough water, carry gear round and float your raft down rapids (on its rope) or build another raft at the bottom.

Always lift raft high on to river bank at night and unload the gear. Beware of flooding during a sudden storm.

Dinghy survival
Avoid leaping into dinghy after ditching or boat wreck. Climb in carefully.

1. **Check everyone is aboard.**
2. **Paddle away from sinking wreck.**
3. **Join up with other dinghies.**
4. **Put out sea anchor.**
5. **Apply first aid.**

Dinghies should link together with 8m (25ft) lines: tie stern of first boat to bows of second and so on. Keep sea anchor line long, and if you lose this anchor substitute a makeshift one at once to stop you drifting away.

Generally aim to stay near crisis site for three days at least for best chance of rescue. During this time:
(a) Retrieve stores / wreckage / buoyancy floating around (but beware sharp metal bits which could spike dinghy floor and buoyancy chamber).
(b) Shelter from bad weather with whatever cover dinghy affords.
(c) Keep watch in two hour stands. Tie person on duty to boat with 6m (20ft) line. He should inspect boat for leaks. Keep bailing. Watch for chance of rescue.

(d) Have signalling gear ready to use immediately.
(e) Ration water and food. Set out solar stills.

Only try to move dinghy out of crisis area if land definitely in reach or sharks attracted by floating food/bodies/remains.

Don't try to sail dinghy unless land is near and downwind. Make sail from anything handy. Inflate raft fully, take in sea anchor and use oar as rudder. Don't secure bottom of sail but hold it with hand-held line so sudden gust doesn't capsize you.

Avoid capsizal (*see Too Wet page 97*) by sitting low in raft in rough weather, keeping sea anchor out, and distributing everyone to ballast the weather side. Don't sit on sides or stand up. When you move warn the others.

Signs of land sometimes are:
Cumulus cloud stationary in clear sky
Green tint in sky above lagoon
Drifting wood
White sky above snowfields (water makes for grey sky)
Lighter colour of water
Roar of surf
Continued bird cries
Bird flight direction in early morning and sunset

If you arrive off land at night, wait until morning to beach if possible. Then select landing point very carefully.

Go to lee of island or point of land. Don't land with sun in your eyes. Steer clear of rocks/reefs/wrecks.

Make for clear gaps in surf. Sloping beach with small surf is ideal. Try to ride in on back of breaker, paddling hard.

Big surf means: keeping on clothes and shoes; checking lifejackets; streaming out sea anchor on as long a line as possible (and keep strain on anchor by adjusting); all hands at the paddles.

Sea anchor will keep you pointing at the shore. Paddle hard to get through oncoming crest and avoid being swept broadside. Try to hold dinghy back from overshooting back of breaker.

Seize raft if you capsize (*see Too Wet page 97*).

Driving

Snow/ice/slush

Drive slowly, gently, and in a higher gear than usual. Take hill in top which you would normally climb in third.

Be alert to lightness of steering. If you have to brake do it on the straight. Pump brakes gently instead of hitting them. Release brake if you skid (*see Too Fast page 216*).

Keep normal tyre inflation on snow. Keep as much weight as possible over driving wheels and stop as little as possible.

Wait until you have a clear run uphill. Avoid trying to climb in too low a gear: over-revving causes wheel-spin. Avoid steep hills where possible.

On banked bends (say on hairpins) where car might slide over edge, travel with wheels on verge or in gutter of far side of any drop.

If wheels start spinning on hill-climb passengers should try jumping up and down inside.

Select low gear to go downhill. Use brakes gently. On very dangerous slopes descend with engine in lowest gear

If trapped in snow (*see Too Cold page 146*).

Through water

Inspect water to see if too deep (height of distributor and carburettor decide this).

(Note: an exhaust pipe extension is useful but not essential.)

Remove fan belt if a lot of water ahead – to stop fan blades drenching engine.

Stop and cool the engine before starting. Then close windows and start through at 5 k.p.h. (3 m.p.h.). Avoid a bow wave piling up against front of car.

Slip clutch if necessary to keep revs fairly high and prevent water entering exhaust pipe, but don't burn out the clutch. Avoid stalling the engine.

Passengers should be ready to jump out and push if wheels start spinning.

A sheet of water ahead can make it impossible to see limits of roadside: you may be driving straight for a river (*see Too Wet page 97*). Watch sides of road when you first inspect water.

Hedges indicate road, but never trust telegraph poles – they may cut across country. Watch ripples from car. They change formation when passing over submerged roadside.

If water swamps car electrics, try this long shot: pull choke right out and fire engine in the hope you can get one cylinder working. If this happens push choke home and keep engine going (in neutral). Eventually other cylinders will join in.

Usually you have to get out and dry leads and distributor with dry cloth. But wait 10 minutes first to let stored-in engine heat do some of the drying too.

Use special aerosol spray for drying if available.

Mud
Avoid wheelspin. Place weight over the driving wheels. Bad patches can be prepared in advance by laying rocks/foliage/sacks. Press throttle slightly.

Don't stop once moving. If wheels start spinning don't rev but reverse smartly.

Mountain pass
Change down in good time for steep gradients. Don't over-rev on hairpins. Choose the easiest line of a very sharp corner – round outside edge.

If radiator boils, switch off engine. Sometimes you can turn car to face the wind. Or freewheel down other side if top already reached. Top up radiator when cool.

If losing power and failing to climb – try ascent in reverse.

Vapour lock in fuel supply (due to overheating) is cured if you:

1. Allow engine to cool; 2. Apply wet cloth to fuel system parts; 3. Prime carburettor by hand.

Sand
Drifts could cover desert tracks.

Keep going at all costs when moving on soft sand until you reach hard ground. Avoid wheelspin (but you may have to change down to first gear as more chance of stalling in top).

Don't stop if engine boils until that hard patch of ground is reached.

If stuck: dig and use jack to slide sandtracks (metal channels/wire mesh/rocks) under wheels.

Sandstorm can be seen approaching. You may be able to drive round it. If no escape: face vehicle away from storm, seal it as well as you can against sand and drive it on to sandtracks.

Wait until storm stops. Don't try to leave vehicle.

Aspects of Travel

Arctic

Travel is extremely strenuous (*see Too Cold page 136*). And very slow.

Salvage gear from aircraft or boat as soon as risk of fire from crash/ditching/landing has passed. Drain oil before it freezes. Remove battery and keep warm. See to clothing/shelter/fire.

Prepare signalling gear while waiting for rescue (*see Too Lonely page 16*).

If you decide to move out head for coast/major river/settlement.

Snowshoes or skis are essential – especially in timber country. Try to travel by river: on raft or dinghy in summer, on ice in winter. But if river very twisting avoid by taking to higher ground ridges.

Keep to inside of bends on river ice. Walk on the far side of junction where rivers meet. Or travel by land until well downriver of the junction. Beware of thin ice all the time.

Check on your tracks behind to help keep on route. Walk 30 paces apart in single file so last man can line up those ahead with compass or by eye to ensure straight travelling in absence of obvious landmarks.

Avoid swamps/tundra lakes/quicksands. Dig into snow and shelter in face of coming blizzard.

Don't leave anyone behind on sea ice. Distant landmarks of ice unreliable for direction-finding as they move. Be ready for ice to break up, ice floes to prove unstable, icebergs to capsize. Keep checking compass (unreliable here) with stars.

Actual texture of ice varies according to season.

Shelter on low-lying, level-topped ice. Don't make rash jumps across water from extreme edges of ice – always leap with about 60cm (2ft) to spare.

Desert

A huge area offering very arduous travel (*see Too Dry page 72*).

Immediate action: take water from transport; wait until any fire-risk from immobilized transport passes; salvage rest of survival gear; relax.

It is vital not to panic and rush in desert heat. Lie in shade and make plans. You should attempt to stay put for at least seven days.

Travel is likely to be over hilly country with unexpected weather changes: windy/freezing/foggy as well as simmering. You should not carry more than 14kg (30lb) weight, yet 4.5 litre (1 gallon) of water weighs 5kg (10lbs). Hence the travel risk.

If some stay and some travel, those walking should take more water than those left waiting for rescue: how much depends on water supplies.

Travellers carry water mainly (plus piece of parachute/groundsheet/polythene for shade, clothing, little food, and navigation aids). Remember torch as you should travel only at night.

(Note: in winter there will be opportunities to travel through days.)

Rest during hot days under double thickness of shelter material rigged bivouac style (*see Too Cold page 145*). Remove shoes and socks when resting (and clean frequently of sand).

Take whatever cover is available in a sandstorm. Button up clothing. If caught in open, lie on ground facing away. Roll occasionally to avoid being buried.

Walk on ridges or troughs between dunes. Steer clear of soft sand where possible. Take care travelling in the dark – sudden slopes are steeper than they look. Develop your night vision.

You must plan route to definite destination. Once you have made a decision don't change it. Set out for road or coast if possible rather than pinpoint a village/oasis/settlement – unless very near.

Jungle

Travel is exacting, but necessary, as tree canopy conceals you from any air search and masks your signals. Ferocious animals, giant spiders, huge snakes and savages are nowhere nearly as dangerous as . . .

Heat exhaustion (*see Too Hot page 172*).

Sickness/fever/poisoning (*see Too Crowded/Too Empty pages 61 and 278*).

Panic (*see Too Lonely page 16*.)

Cross country travel very difficult. Follow rivers (both wet and dry), game trails, native paths, ridges. But never follow water too closely downhill as it takes shortest route down waterfalls/defiles/gullies.

When you find a trail – follow it. Good places for this: river crossing; low hill passes; river rapids. You may see natives here (*see Too Crowded page 50*). Native villages are sited on stream banks.

Main jungle equipment – water (refill containers whenever possible), machette or knife, compass, strong shoes, hammock and shelter, first-aid kit.

Trust compass more than maps. Check it with night sky. Sun rises too high in day to be accurate guide, except early in morning and late afternoon. Follow water when without compass.

Detour any dense foliage/swamps/ravines. Don't travel at night when trails mentioned above are used by animals and reptiles. Always take easiest line.

You are soaked with rain and sweat in jungle. Body moisture and vital salts are lost. Keep drinking (and taking salt). Defy heat exhaustion (*see Too Hot page 172*).

If separated from companions bang a stick against tree trunks – the noise carries further than shouting. Take action if lost and separated from companions (*see earlier*). But this should never happen. Stick together.

Watch for trees with octopus-like roots and avoid swamp they indicate. Also beware of falling deadwood/coconuts/animals by looking up often.

Make plenty of noise to warn animals (like beating on trunks). Travel in single file with front man breaking trail with machette or knife.

Avoid rotting logs/stumps/branches – they harbour ticks. Beware of crocodile risk when faced with water. Don't blunder into hornets nest. Be alert.

Fig 73   Bivouac and hammock

Rest often. And stop well before dark to make camp.
(a) Choose solid ground, not marshy. Avoid dead-wood above you. Check flooding risk. Clear ground completely of vegetation.
(b) Sleep off ground in hammock or on raised bed of branches and leaves. Simplest design resembles small four-poster bed with parachute canopy completely draped over. Simple bivouac shelter (*see Too Cold page 145*) is good general shelter too.
(c) Build thorn fence round camp if uneasy. Keep fire lit all night. Wrap up well against cold.
(d) Scatter ash from fire round camp to stop insects crawling in.

Any amount of improvisation can be carried out with wood and huge leaves in jungle with knife or sharp stones. Leaves are a good shelter thatch. Bamboo makes fishhooks/harpoons/furniture. Ferns, vines, canes, weeds and flowers can often produce string/twine/cord.

Mountain
Avoid mountain ranges when possible (*see Too High/Too Low/Too Cold pages 198, 192 and 136*). Especially

when snow-capped and presenting glaciers and avalanche possibilities.

If no rope, no ice axe for each person, no experi-
enced leader give a wide berth. If no alternative: travel
in early morning when snow and ice is frozen hard.
Beware once sun starts to melt slopes.

Travel Hazards

Frostbite
Exposure } *see Too Cold (page 157)*
Trench foot

Heat Exhaustion
Sunstroke } *see Too Hot (page 172)*

Sun blindness
Sunburn } *see Too Bright (page 117)*

Blisters
Don't break foot blisters. As soon as skin reddens
apply a plaster (if available). Edges can be pricked with
flame-sterilized point. Press fluid out gently. Dry with
improvised bandage. If very painful rest until better.

Prevention: wash/rinse/dry stockings each night.
Darn holes immediately (and carefully). Always keep
change of socks if possible.

Hot salt water bath is comforting.

Rashes
Soothe irritation from poisonous plants with – if nothing else – coconut oil, or paste of wood ash and
water. Bandage.

A good tan (gained under hot sun for 5 minutes
exposure only daily) is best protection against prickly
heat and sunburn.

Seasickness
Concentrate on some job. If bad don't eat and drink.
Lie still, keep changing head position. Keep warm.
Take seasickness tablets if available.

Salt water sores
Keep body as dry as possible. Don't open or squeeze

sores. Clean gently. Cover large sores with dressing.
Antiseptic cream OK if you have it.

Constipation

Expect it when short on food and water. Don't use
laxatives – and rob body of moisture. Also expect dark
urine (difficult to pass). Don't sweat about it.

Cracked lips/parched skin

Use oil/salve/chapstick or any suncream if handy.

Too
Full

13 Too Full

When your world explodes – be it with bomb/
hurricane/erupting volcano – what can anyone possibly do in the face of such total destruction?

Flash and fire, blast and radiation fall-out, or a sky
darkening so rapidly with hot ash that thousands of
kilometres/miles away a magnifying glass will no longer set fire to a piece of paper because the sun is
screened by pumice dust as a result . . . Everyone can
be affected.

Benjamin Franklin discovered erupting volcanoes
might prevent a struggling survivor on the other side
of the globe from lighting such a fire in 1783. In the
1980s this risk still exists, but there are now so many
more new and vastly menacing threats closer to home,
any of which can make your perhaps humdrum exist-
ence all too full of activity within a moment. *Yet
knowing about these may help.*

Letter/Parcel Bombs

All you can do with such a missive is to suspect it
before you try opening it any further . . .

Here are some possible clues.

*Any current wave of terrorist activity in region/city/
country*
Book-sized parcels rather than small ones
Anything from unusual sources
Items addressed in a foreign or unknown style of writing
Springiness inside a pack or envelope
Lopsided feel
Wires sticking through paper
Smell of marzipan
Greasy marks from explosive sweating
*Rattling loose metallic sounds (like a safety pin/drawing
pin/needle).*
Unusual amount of stamps
Additional envelope inside tied with string/tape/staples

If a parcel or envelope arouses your suspicions . . .

1. **Put it down at once.**
2. **Call the police.**
3. **Resist temptation to slit the paper a little.**
4. **Do not put package in sand or water.**

Earthquakes

Without any advance warning possible, the motion of an earthquake may herald absolute extinction – or merely near it. You won't know until too late. There are two main risks besides the ground possibly opening under your feet – falling masonry *and* widespread fire.

1. **Keep inside, off the streets and away from windows.**
2. **Stand inside a doorway to take advantage of its overhead support (or squeeze under a strong desk/table/bench).**
3. **Wait until police give the all-clear.**

If inside a car much depends on if you can drive out or not. If not, get down on to the floor and wait the emergency out.

Hurricanes and Big Storms

Heed all warnings of imminent abnormal weather conditions. From TV/radio/your own observations.

1. **Stay at home***
2. **Barricade windows (with heavy furniture if necessary).**
3. **Store away all loose objects outside (dustbins/garden tools/toys).**
4. **Take valuables out from rooms where windows may break.**
5. **Have flashlights/food/drinking water/empty buckets ready just in case services fail or water comes in through the roof.**
6. **Avoid touching electrical appliances if wet.**
7. **Keep listening to weather reports.**

* Hurricanes cause tidal waves that sweep inland. Get

away from low areas that may be flooded by the sea, lake or river. Drive with topped-up fuel tank. This can happen in many countries – not just USA.

Quarry Blasting

If you live near a quarry that warns of an extra-large blast, then take precautions. Houses and people can be affected by the blast for kilometres/miles.

1. **Open all windows before the appointed time.**
2. **If in the vicinity open your mouth at countdown time . . .**
3. **And press fingers in ears.**

The purpose of the two actions is the same. In the one, to save burst eardrums; in the other, shattered glass.

Erupting Volcanoes

The following signs should give ample warning . . .

Local earthquakes . . . rivers with sulpherous smell . . . steam hanging over a mountain or hill peak . . . rumbling sounds . . . acid rain . . . pumice dust in the sky . . . hot ashes and gasses issuing from the hill.

Leaving the area is the only answer – and certainly if the volcano finally erupts. Car fuel tanks should be full. But cars are no guarantee you can escape once ash is raining down. Be ready to walk using makeshift mask over mouth and nose. Protect the head if possible from flying stones/rocks/pebbles.

Buildings in the locality will be dangerous: roofs bombarded by rocks will often collapse.

Your only escape is to flee – and fast.

The Bomb

No one is immune from or necessarily doomed by nuclear bomb attack (it could miss a target to hit theoretically safe ground). Take precautions on the chance you are outside the explosion area.

Bomb Effects

Flash-heat
See Too Bright/Too Hot pages 113 and 169.

Blast
Like thunder follows lightning, blast follows flash – almost immediately or possibly over a minute later. The force will uproot trees/flatten buildings/make people into missiles in the devastation area. And still wreak damage outside it.

Radiation Fall-Out

The explosion churns wreckage into dust which is sucked up into the fireball – and then released as deadly contaminated dust. Every bit dropping back is radio-active.

Fall-out will fill the explosion area within an hour and then – depending on wind directions/speed/variability – blanket a huge area. Invisible, fall-out will kill and sicken. It can only be detected by instruments carried by civil defence/police/services.

Warnings

Period of increasing tension in the daily news is first likely indication. Official instructions will be given by radio/TV/Press/noticeboards if things get really bad.

Warnings of potential attack are graded by colour.

1. 'Red': sirens rising and falling (attack imminent).
2. 'Grey': sirens'/bells'/whistles' interrupted note of steady pitch (fall-out expected in an hour).
3. 'Black': rockets/gongs/whistles sounding morse 'D' dash dot dot (fall-out imminent).

The all-clear is sirens on a steady note.

What to Do When Warned

Bad news
Make home as fire-proof (*see Too Bright/Too Hot pages 113 and 169*) and fall-out proof as possible. Working

fast you can do a great deal towards this in a day. Stock up with supplies.

If you live in bungalow, single storey pre-fabricated house or caravan try to join families in more substantial dwellings.

Middle floors of multi-storey flats are the safest, while ground and top floors (especially top) are unsafe. Occupants here should join families on middle floors if possible.

Flats four storeys high or less, however, are only safe on the ground floor.

Red warning
Those who cannot reach home in a matter of minutes should shelter in nearest safe building. If in open fling yourself on ground (*see Too Bright page 113*).

If you are indoors: switch off electricity, gas, and water (at mains stopcock). Then shut everyone inside the fall-out refuge (*see page 259*).

Once explosion happens and you are still alive, check fire-risk immediately (*see Too Hot page 169*). Cover up well with clothing when you do this, then shed outer clothes before entering fall-out refuge.

Grey warning
Try to reach good cover before fall-out comes in the hour. Your shelter needs thick walls and roof and stopped-up windows and doors to keep radiation at a distance.

Move quickly, keeping calm. Avoid fall-out contact at all costs.

Grey warning does not mean another attack will not follow meanwhile. Don't expose yourself needlessly to attack.

Black warning
If you are still outside and have missed all previous warnings go for cover at once, throwing off outer clothes and leaving them outside when you find shelter.

If possible wash exposed parts of body and brush down rest of clothing before entering cover.

Stay inside until told by police or civil defence to move. Listen to radio announcements. You may be able to leave fall-out refuge for other parts of the building on essential errands – but not for first three days (when fall-out most potent) unless absolutely essential.

Rely on official instructions as to when, where and how to go. And for how long.

Advance Preparations

Preparing against first flash-heat wave (*see Too Bright/ Too Hot pages 113 and 169*).

Making a fall-out refuge

Effects of fall-out can be weakened by three factors.

1. **Distance**
2. **Thickness**
3. **Time**

Choose cellar/room/passage with fewest outside walls. Try to buttress walls/windows/doors with as much extra thickness as possible. Bricks, concrete, hard-packed earth all baffle fall-out attack.

(a) Hole in ground outdoors (roofed with boards and soil), cellar or basement gives best protection.
(b) Room on ground floor of house with as little outside wall as possible can be used. Or an interior passage. The further away from outside walls and roof you are the better.
(c) Thinly protected house can give some shelter if you build a fall-out refuge core (*see page 261*).

Put as much distance between you and the outside of the houses as possible. Strengthen and thicken all round the refuge. Take out windows and fill spaces with double layer of bricks, or board up and pack in between with pressed-down soil. Wire or bolt boards together.

Pile up heavy furniture/books/sandbags against windows, doors and walls. Block windows and doors of rooms and/or passages leading to fall-out refuge. Pile sandbags/earth boxes/oil drums on outside of refuge walls. Deep snow also helps.

An outdoor trench deep enough for family to stand

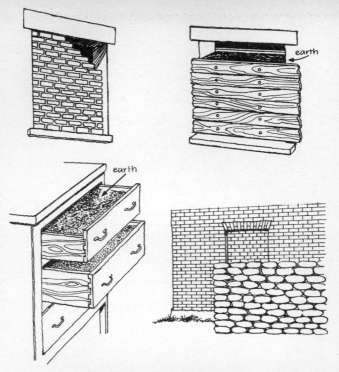

Fig 74   House strengthening

Fig 75   Outdoor Fall-out shelter

Fig 76 Fall-out shelter cores

in is very effective. Shore sides with improvised pit props. Cover top with planks/metal sheeting/concrete slabs, then pile and press down soil on top.

Keep tools inside (in case you have to dig out). Manhole entrance through roof can be covered with dustbin lid (covered on top with anything convenient).

If you make passage it may collapse under blast. Jam sandbags to prop its roof and combat radiation.

Making refuge core
Build another shelter inside refuge to give extra protection (especially during first three days of fall-out). It can vary from tent of sandbags to a lean-to formed by doors propped against the wall and covered with sandbags, cushions filled with earth, plastic bags full of soil.

An underfloor trench covered over is effective. So is cupboard under the stairs with sandbags covering all stairs and built up outside the walls.

After three days, worst of fall-out could be over, allowing you to live in rest of refuge before going outdoors at (approximately) the end of ten days.

Stocking up

Use a check list of equipment needed in refuge. You must be self-sufficient. Don't take so much stuff that the place becomes cluttered but use common sense.

Remember you will be using this small place for sleeping/eating and as bathroom and lavatory. A radio is essential. So is plenty of fresh water and food (all kept in screwed-up containers). Hygiene is very important too.

Food and water

Supplies should last three weeks at least.

Food and water is *not* contaminated by radiation rays passing through. But it will be contaminated once fall-out dust collects on it.

Always wipe down food and water containers before opening. Water kept in open-topped containers (like the bath) must be covered, and the top wiped down before it is lifted off.

Remember – it is essential to cut off mains water immediately *red* warning is heard so contaminated supply cannot enter and spoil water already in your cistern/lavatory/pipes.

Keep at least three days' supply of water (which is more important than food) in refuge core. Wipe down and take care when opening container so no fall-out dust can spill inside.

A search for food outdoors (*see Too Empty page 266*) following fall-out period means you must look for foods naturally protected – like nuts, say, which are shielded by the shell. *When possible check foods with authorities*. Wear gloves when handling.

(a) Eggs will probably be safe to eat – especially if hens stayed under cover during fall-out.

(b) Wash and peel potatoes (fall-out contamination is not removed by cooking alone). Cook.

262

(c) Peas and beans protected by their pods would be edible.

(d) Greens like cabbages/sprouts/lettuces are fairly safe. Pick the heart and discard all outer leaves. Note: heart must be solid and have been shielded by outer leaves.

(e) Fish will probably be safe to eat.

(f) No animals which have been roaming outside through fall-out period will be really safe.

But after first few days of fall-out there is a risk of plants being contaminated by their roots taking up radioactive materials in the soil.

If food so scarce you must eat growing plants (and there is no chance of having them tested) eat in this order: (1) potatoes, (2) peas, (3) beans, (4) greens.

Water in mains supply will be contaminated. And rainwater too. Boiling water does not make it fit to drink. Water in wells/caves/tanks will probably be drinkable however.

(Note: when going outside after fall-out has faded follow official instructions on safety precautions. Dress so outer clothing can still be left outside shelter on return – including shoes and gumboots. Always wear gloves indoors or out when handling anything that could have been contaminated by fall-out.)

Radiation Sickness

Could be slight or serious. Signs: sickness, weakness, nausea, diarrhoea, loss of appetite, possibly delirium.

Treat wounds or other injuries; remove all contaminated clothing where possible and wash patient – remembering the hair. Wear gloves/long coat/mask.

Keep patient's clothing and washing water separate from anything else to avoid contamination danger.

Await help from police/civil defence/services.

Nuclear Spills

People living near nuclear power stations are vulnerable if radio-active material escapes. The main danger: radio-active iodine leaked in the atmosphere and being absorbed by the human thyroid gland which, in approx. 30 years, might result in cancer.

Remedy: swallow a couple of K-1 pills – small, brown, sharp-tasting potassium iodate pills (they fill the thyroid with so much harmless iodine there's no room left for the radio-active variety that might exist outside).

Police stockpile these pills near nuclear power stations/nuclear reprocessing plants/nuclear-powered ships and submarines, ready to distribute them in times of emergency – to homes downwind of any nuclear leakage.

Otherwise, when you receive word via radio/TV/ police public address systems – *see Advance Preparations/Radiation Fall-out pages 113, 169 and 256.*

Too
Empty

14   Too Empty

Hunger alone does not kill. Man can stay alive several weeks without solid food, but he will grow so weak he becomes increasing prey to sickness/disease/elements.

After his ordeal a survivor's condition will depend on what he found to eat. And how he overcame his distaste of accessible meals like cockroaches, frog, nettles, birds.

To detail what is *safe* to eat would take books (there are over 300,000 plants alone). What basic rules can the survivor follow to stave off starvation when on the spot?

Live Off the Land

Eat as much and whenever possible (unless short of water). Try for one hot meal a day minimum.

Keep in reserve whatever food you already have (follow directions on survival food packs). Spin it out by the food you find.

Grass. Ferns. Tree bark. Eggs. Shellfish. Slugs. Candles. Lizards. Frogs. Seaweed. Squirrels. Crickets. Rats. Termites. Grasshoppers. Seagulls. And thousands more.

Stick mainly to plant-eating when short on water. Plants won't increase thirst as much as fish/meat/eggs (*see Too Dry page 74*).

If it moves – consider it potentially rich food. Exceptions: all toads, some shellfish, some saltwater fish, and parts of various creatures like the liver of polar bears and seals, skin of salamanders, heads of snakes.

How to Eat Unpleasant Food

Shut eyes, pinch nose – and chew! The difference is amazing. Raw potato tastes like a Golden Delicious apple.

Plants

Test

1. **Plant must not irritate skin/stink/have milky juice.**
2. **Bite off small piece.**
3. **Hold piece inside lower lip for five minutes.**
4. **Eat this if no soapy/bitter/burning taste.**
5. **If no ill effects within ten hours plant is safe.**

Some plants which are safe to eat won't pass this test (*see later*), but majority of plants do.

Small quantity of poisonous food is unlikely to kill or make you seriously ill whereas large dose will. Once plant passes test don't eat large quantities at once, but gradually increase quantities.

Plants eaten by birds and animals are not always safe for humans. Test these plants as you would any other before eating in quantity.

Avoid mushrooms – unless you know them to be safe.

All plants should be cooked for safety – especially when you are not sure. But poisonous mushrooms are not made safe by cooking.

Experiment with best parts of plants to eat; fruit; bark; sap; tubers; roots; seeds; pods; flowers; buds; nuts; leaves; stems; bulbs; shoots.

Fig 77   Poisonous plants, left to right: deadly nightshade, yew, hemlock

Widespread plants
Universally-found edible plants (*see later for plants special to areas*) are:
(a) Grasses (including rice/oats/wheat). Help grass on

to cloth and beat out seeds with stick. Rub/shred/ blow chaff away and pound seeds in container. Boil or roast (avoid black and withered seeds). Stems are edible too.

(b) Nuts everywhere can be eaten. Bitter taste can be washed away by swilling mashed-up nuts in a stream.

(c) Tree bark (inner layers) are edible boiled/roasted/ chewed raw. Avoid only if unpleasantly bitter.

(d) Berries should be tested carefully first – they may be poisonous even though birds eat them.

(e) Ferns (especially the young coils) are a safe stand-by. Scrub away hairs in water and boil.

(f) Elephant grass (in all damp areas) grows taller than a man and has seeds like firework sparklers. Boil roots/flowers/shoots.

(g) Bamboo has many edible parts: seeds/shoots/ roots. This grass grows from tall swamp grasses to trees over 33m (100ft) high. And grows wherever really moist and warm.

(h) Seaweed clinging to rocks or floating is edible when healthy/fresh/firm (though will make you thirsty). Leave slimy, decaying seaweed alone.

(i) Lichens can be scraped/peeled/crumbled off rock and soaked well in water. Boil.

Hunting

Small animals and insects are your most likely bet. View hunting with common sense. Don't expect success at first. But something to come slowly with practice.

Weapons
Use everything. Catapults powered by underpants-elastic or hide from already dead animals. Clubs/ bludgeons/spears. Knives. Rock missiles. Sling/bow-and-arrow/gun.

Keep knives sharp. Any sandstone will do this, but gray soft sandstone better than quartz (which will scratch knife blade with bright scars).

Granite (rubbed smooth on another granite lump) will also sharpen knives. Hold blade at slight angle on stone and push away, sharpening sides alternately.

Keep guns clean. Never clog the barrel – or try to shoot out an obstruction. Clean barrel with hot water and pull through piece of cloth on string.

In arctic-cold clean all oil off gun. Wrap it well against any contact with snow or ice. Leave wrapped outside a warm shelter.

Going for the kill

Least subtle approach best when inexperienced. Arm companions with clubs and/or net. Surround area of bush. Set fire to target and attack creatures which run out. If no fire, converge, trampling down undergrowth.

Other variations: set fire to hollow tree; poke sticks down holes having sealed off as many other exits from a warren as you can find; or light fire at burrow entrance. Wait with weapons for animal exit.

Fire catapult/sling/gun as close to target as possible. Aim to make one shot do the job. And fire from steadiest position you can find.

Shoulder/chest/head are best all-round targets of game. If animal/bird/reptile falls re-load immediately and be ready for it to get up and run.

Try to catch your target lying/sitting/standing. This needs very careful approach:

(a) Discover where animals pass. Signs are droppings, tracks, trampled ground. Best areas: water/forest clearings/edges of thickets.

(b) Avoid the trail or runway itself once discovered. Prepare to hunt in early morning or dusk.

(c) Hide with face to wind or the slightest breeze. If sun shining keep it behind you if possible.

(d) Keep still.

(e) *Crawl* forward only when animal is feeding/drinking/looking away. As soon as it starts to turn head, freeze.

(f) Avoid snapping twigs, brushing aside foliage, silhouetting yourself.

Try night hunting with a light. It can attract creatures giving you chance to strike/club/spear. You will develop various methods with practice – like stalking a frog with one hand while grabbing with the other.

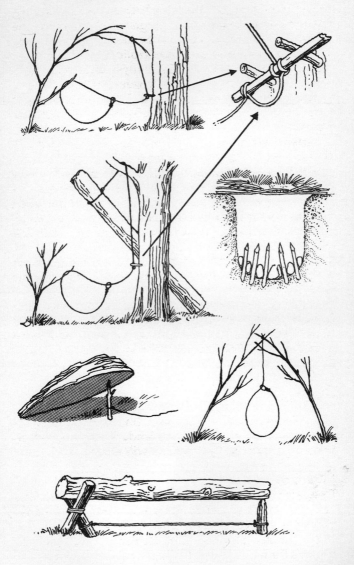

Fig 78   Traps and triggers

Trapping

Success is bound to be hit-and-miss until you are well practiced. But you may be lucky. Make a determined search for signs of wild life in your region.

Use lots of snares/traps/deadfalls to capture, strangle or crush wild creatures. Diagrams show principles of how these work and can be improvised, but use common sense. For instance saplings bent over and tied to a snare may not budge if triggered by animal in very cold weather (trees are frozen stiff).

Keep traps simple and small. You are unlikely to trap big animals with cumbersome and elaborate deadfalls.

Elastic/cord/wire are essentials. So are *natural*-looking traps. Lay them across narrowest part of trails and runways. Or narrow-down a wide trail with rocks/foliage/herbage – so long as it looks part of area.

Lie in cover, keep still, watch for signs of life when you have found tracks. One kind of animal life usually means other forms around too. Snares can be hand-held ready to pull.

(Note: snares across tracks or over animal burrows should admit creature's head but be too small for the body.)

Wild life can be attracted towards a trap by kissing back of hand to make loud squeaks.

Butcher a trapped animal on the spot and leave entrails. These may attract other animals within several hours. Re-spring trap.

Fishing

Most fish are edible – poisonous ones are found mainly in tropical waters close to land. Remember when short of water that eating fish will increase thirst.

Where to look

Deepest parts of rivers. Pools below rapids in shallow streams. Behind and under rocks. Below the bank. Underneath falls. Experiment at all likely places.

Fish with outgoing tide. Remember one of best regions for food is between high and low water mark.

Fish in early morning or dusk. Fish are attracted by a light. Flying fish can be landed on a raft by reflecting

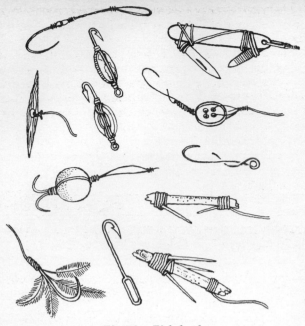

Fig 79   Fish-hooks

torch or moonlight onto sail/shirt/sheet and catching them as they jump.

Shrimps, prawns, crabs, crayfish can be caught by combination of shining a light, searching shallow waters and using nets.

Watch swimming habits of fish, type of food they are likely to go for, then use your ingenuity to net/hook/trap them.

Catching fish
Line and hook can be improvised with cloth or plant fibres and bent pin (though proper hooks much better). Try different lures: feathers/plastic/fish entrails or bright cloth, metal or worms.

Hooks can be made from bone/wire/wood. Stop fishing line being bitten through by attaching hook to line with thin wire.

Jerk heavy metal bait up and down in water to attract fish. (Hooks and lure must be heavy enough to sink quickly.)

A small kite (*see Too Lonely page 16*) will carry a fishing line well out over the water and increases your chances. Rig fishing line to kite line with bent pin at one place only – and so any tension (from biting fish) to fishing line will jerk it free. Or you release it yourself.

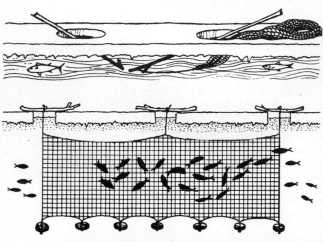

Fig 80   Fixing gill net under ice

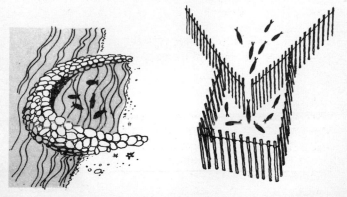

Fig 81   Fish-traps

Other methods:

(a) Catch by tickling fish under rocks with bare hands. Then scoop out.

(b) Wade into shallow water and club/spear/net fish. Or do it from the bank.

(c) Stun fish in pools and ponds by burning coral or seashells to make lime and throwing into water.

(d) Make nets from whatever line/string/cordage handy. Parachute cloth net for shrimping. Closemesh net can be stretched out across stream between two of you walking quickly through it lifting rocks in water, snatching net out frequently with a possible catch each time.

A gill net hangs in still lake/river/sea water and traps fish swimming through it. Fix under ice as shown with branches/sticks/poles and patience. Set net at right angles to shore. Use stones for weights and wood/rubber cork/for float.

(e) Fish traps can be made from rocks and sticks (as shown). Check movements of schools of fish. Sea fish often move in with the tide and swim along the shore. Lake fish come towards banks in morning and at dusk.

Pick trap site at high tide and build at low. Make it look at much a part of the scenery as possible.

Use any natural features – spits/reefs/ledges – as part of trap. Look at it from fish's viewpoint.

Nets work all the time, and traps store fish fresh and live until you need them. They could prove worth the trouble they are to make.

Catches to throw back

1. **Beware fish with flabby skin/slimy gills/sunken eyes.**

2. **Beware if fish stinks.**

3. **Beware if dent from pressed-in thumb stays in fish.**

Other danger signs are: naked or bony skin instead of scales; fish that puffs up as it is taken from water; fish covered in spikes/thorns/bristles (which can give you poisonous wound).

Also throw back netted jellyfish/diamond-shaped rays with long tails/sea snakes (they have flat tails).

Keep off black mussels.

Never collect dead shellfish – when touched shellfish should move and/or grip rocks tighter. Don't try shellfish with cone or spindle-shaped shells.

Cooking

1. **Clean food soon after collecting.**
2. **Always cook when possible.**
3. **Dry extra meat or fish over fire or in sun.**

Remove poisonous parts of creature at once (say head of snake). Slit animal's stomach and roll skin backwards like taking off glove. Scrap skin and guts.

Shellfood   (clams/oysters/mussels/crabs/crayfish) should be left overnight in clean water to clean themselves.

Scale and wash fish in clean water. Cut out gills and slit underside. Chop head off.

Boiling is best way of cooking in survival situations. If possible drink the cooking water too. Boil seafood in seawater. Add plants to fish or meat stews.

If no cooking pot available use improvised spit or fork to roast over coals. Or wrap in clay/mud/wet leaves and bake among hot embers – don't clean or skin food before baking. Or make utensils from inner layers of birch bark (as shown).

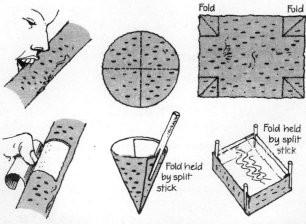

Fig 82   Inner birch bark utensils

If no fire available in very cold conditions let food freeze, then carve off thin shavings, warming it to just below freezing before eating.

Storing Food

Keep fish alive in trap until you need it. Or store in box underwater. Once dead – like meat – cut into strips and dry under hot sun or firesmoke if unable to boil it straight away.

Cover food. Wrap it against insect and animal contamination. Hang on trees out of animal reach.

Use damp packing: shellfish in seaweed; berries/fruit/roots in sphagnum moss, wet leaves. Keep food cool in holes in ground/banks/rocks. Wet cloth hole cover acts as cooler. Food stays fresh buried in snow or sand (but mark the spot).

Wipe off mould on stored meat. In wet conditions smoked or sun-dried meat and fish need drying out to prevent mould. In hot weather re-cook once-cooked animal food once a day.

Best safeguard of all against food poisoning is to eat *fresh* food and cook it.

Aspects of Food Finding

Arctic
You need more food in cold climate than in hot. Yet here food can be very scarce (although plentiful in sub-arctic areas).

Marmots, squirrels, rabbits, hare, porcupine, muskrat, rats, beaver, geese – all possible prey. Obviously avoid the big food (polar bears) unless you have gun, skill and courage.

Fishing through ice is determined by whether you can find a place thin enough to hack through. Use line or net (*see page 272*).

Vegetation is sometimes abundant, sometimes hidden. Watch where birds land. Many safe plants but two very dangerous ones: baneberry (red/white/blue berries growing in clusters) and water hemlock (parsley family plant growing 1.2–2.4m (4–8ft) high with purply leaves which stink when bruised).

Eat lichens/seaweed/roots/greens/berries. But leave fungi alone.

Desert
Food should only be eaten in small doses when water is short (*see Too Dry page 74*).

Plant food is rare. Try cacti fruit/roots/leaves (with spikes removed). Greenest grass is food source too. Avoid plants with milky sap.

Gazelle/antelope/birds sometimes seen near water. But most likely animal foods are snakes/rats/lizards/slugs/locusts – if you are lucky.

Desert islands
Seafood is most reliable – so long as non-poisonous. Clams, mussels, sea cucumbers, crabs, sea urchins crayfish, shrimps can be found on shore and in coral reef pockets.

Avoid black mussels and shellfish with cone-shaped or spindly shells.

Follow turtle tracks on sand. Turtles can be rolled on their backs (watch claws and mouth), head cut off and baked. Eggs may be buried near sea and 60cm (2 ft) under sand.

Even barren islands often have edible weeds – some with yellow flowers tasting like watercress. Coconut palms and screw pine palms (with good fruit looking like pineapples) found on otherwise bare islands too.

Jungle
Many foods are available in jungle, though hard to find in rain forest. Old native gardens (abandoned) are excellent food source. Test all plants you try (as earlier).
(a) Coconuts are a standby for food (*see Too Dry page 79*).
(b) Sago palm has spiny trunk. Grind up pith under bark, soak in water, strain and bake residue.
(c) Taro roots/leaves/stalks must be boiled. Leaves are shaped like elephant ears.
(d) Papaya is marrow-shaped fruit on palm-type tree (avoid leaves which have milky sap).
(e) Mangoes also exception to milky sap rule. They

grow on knobbly trees with dense canopy, and resemble large pears.

(f) Figs (edible grow on milky sap trees).

(g) Breadfruit (milky sap) looks like yellowy-green melon on leathery-leaved tree.

(h) Yams (like potatoes) have to be dug from under plants with gigantic and coarse leaves.

Bananas/sugar cane/pineapple add to the wide tropical edible plants ranging from bamboo and grass to water lilies and ferns.

Avoid:

Milky sap plants apart from exceptions mentioned
Fungi
Plants which irritate/burn/wound your skin
Anything tasting foul
Plants resembling tomatoes
Brightly-coloured fruits and berries

Monkeys' food is a fairly reliable pointer to safe human food, but still test first.

Small creatures (frogs, lizards, snakes, insects, grubs, birds) much more likely to provide meals than big game.

Mountains
Very little food on high ridges besides lichens and birds. Descend below treeline to eat.

Hunger Hazards

Poisoning
Need not be in the wilds. If not, telephone doctor immediately. Do what he says.

Otherwise drink lots of water (or milk) to dilute. Make yourself vomit by sticking fingers down throat. Salt and water (warmed) do same job.

After vomiting, drink more milk. Four glasses say.

Note: if poisoned by acid, alkali (ammonia), petrol or paraffin don't try to be sick. Acid = two teaspoonfuls of magnesia in glass of water; alkalis = teaspoonful of vinegar in glass of water; petrol and paraffin = lots of glasses of water.

Cannibalism

All kinds of things become either sinful or acceptable when economic or political expediency demand. Men and women have forced themselves to overcome man's deepest taboo when the need arose. Can they be blamed? Or should they be praised for their determination to live?

(When you, alive and kicking, could become victim *see Too Crowded page 36*.)

A Last Chance

Can you be sure someone *is* dead?

Not always. It can puzzle even medical people sometimes. Example: people suffering extreme exposure (*see Too Cold page 157*) resemble corpses. Look at the hours and hours it has sometimes taken to bring round an apparently had-it person with artificial respiration.

In certain cases signs of death can be misleading if taken individually. Blue lips might simply mean blockage in airways. Waxy skin (or pallor) could just be caused by bleeding. Heart beats may be missing – if you are not feeling in the right place (to do this: place pads of fingertips on skin of lower left chest and feel over a wide region).

Play safe. Look for as many signs of death as possible, thus:

No heartbeat
No pulse
Blue lips
Pallor
Muscles stiff
Bowel movement
Mouth agape
Dilated pupils
Pupils don't move in torchlight
Eyes glazed
Body cold
Muscle stays flat after pressed
Skin stained red-blue in parts
No blurring on mirror held to nose/mouth

Unless no doubt at all that person is dead, keep up artificial respiration/keeping them warm/getting help quickly. Or whatever else circumstances dictate. And *really keep it up* – right to the bitter end.

Index

This index anticipates disasters that may befall you – by directing you to the necessary help *before* you need it . . . before you approach any likely disaster point which, no matter how mundane it may seem *now* (whether ball game/train trip/rush hour roundabout), might turn sour at the flick of a finger.

285